A Gazeteer o

CW00801586

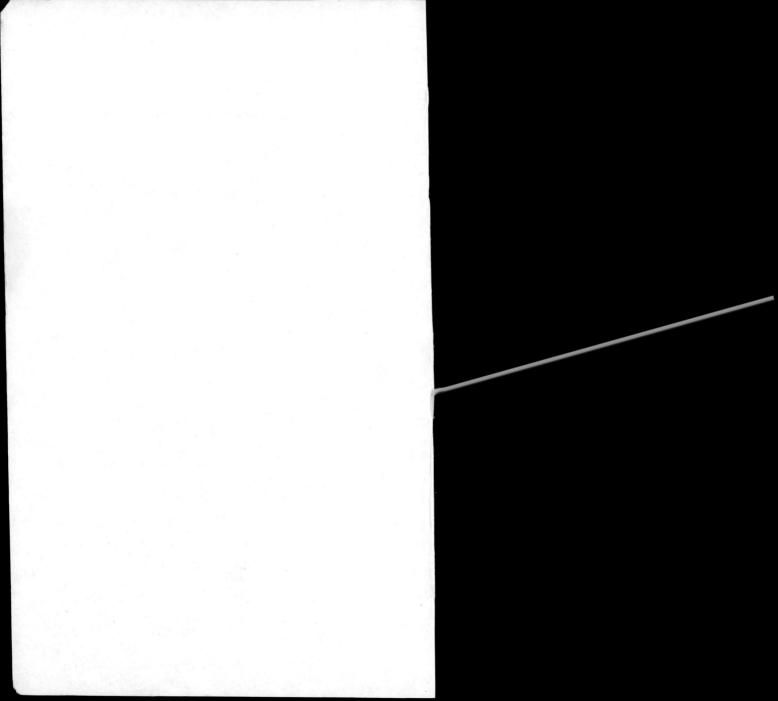

A Gazeteer of the
Welsh Slate Industry

Alun John Richards

GWASG CARREG GWALCH

ISBN: 0-86381-196-5

Maps by K. Lloyd Gruffydd

Cover photo:
Prince of Wales Quarry
(see page 101)

Acknowledgements

I am grateful for the practical and documentary assistance of:
David Gwynn, Gwynfor P. Jones, Michael Lewis, Lewis Lloyd, Merfyn
Williams, Richard Williams and many others including the Staff and
Friends of Plas Tan y Bwlch. With particular thanks to the constant
encouragement of my wife.

First published in 1991 by Gwasg Carreg Gwalch,

Dedicated to all those that worked and still work in the Slate quarries of Wales, and especially to those many who suffered death, disablement or disease in this great and proud industry.

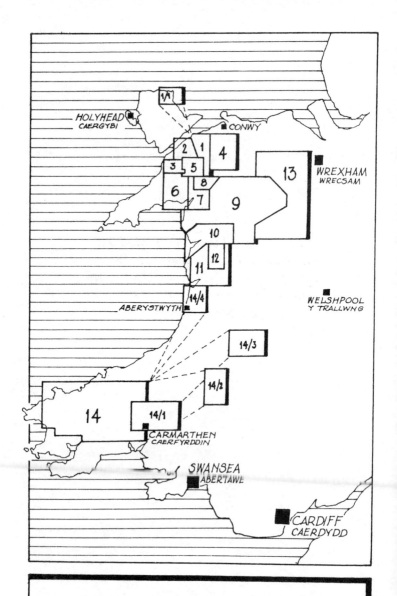

SECTION LOCATION MAP

CONTENTS

Alun John Richards, a retired engineer besides spending many years investigating the Archaeology of the Welsh Slate Industry, has been responsible for several technical innovations in Welsh slate quarries. He is a Guest Tutor on Slate at the Snowdonia National Park Study Centre, Plas Tan y Bwlch and is co-founder and past chairman of the Friends of Tan y Bwlch.

Rhagair

Ychydig ohonom sydd yn sylweddoli pa mor eang yw dosbarthiad y Diwydiant Llechi yng Nghymru. Rydym yn gyfarwydd gyda chwareli mawrion agored Arfon neu chwareli tanddaearol Meirion ond, yn ei anterth, roedd y diwydiant ar waith yng Nghlwyd, Dyfed a Powys hefyd.

Y mae nifer o bobl wedi ysgrifennu am y chwareli ond canolbwyntio y maent, gan fwyaf, ar eu 'milltir sgwâr chwarelyddol'. Cawn enghreifftiau o hanes chwarel a'r cymeriadau yn gysylltiedig â hi. Ychydig a gawn o ddisgrifiadau *Archeoleg Diwydiannol* y diwydiant sef yr astudiaeth o olion gweladwy y chwareli — ambell adeilad, tramffordd, rhôd ddŵr a thomen.

Dyma yw priod faes Alun Richards. Nid oes neb yn gwybod am olion chwareli Cymru benbaladr cystal ag ef. Yr Archeoleg Diwydiannol y chwareli yw ei fan cychwyn. I gyflawni y gwaith y mae wedi treulio blynyddoedd yn tramwyo i fannau anghysbell i recordio ymgais mwyaf di-nod o ran llwyddiant ond efallai gyda nodweddion archeolegol mwyaf diddorol. Yn gwmni iddo ar y llafur cariad yma o'r cychwyn bu ei wraig, Delphine.

Y mae cyfraniad Alun Richards i'n dealltwriaeth ni o'n treftadaeth diwydiannol wedi bod yn fawr a dyma gyrraedd penllanw ei waith gyda chwblhau y cyfeiriadur cyntaf o'r diwydiant mwyaf Cymreig a Chymraeg Cymru.

Merfyn Williams,
Ael y Bryn,
Croesor.

Foreword

This sets out to be a guide to the buildings and other artifacts that exist on the various sites in Wales where slate was extracted, with some emphasis on their transport arrangements, since good transport was, and still is, an integral part of the Industry.

It does not set out to be more than a superficial framework for fieldwork study. Several reports have been prepared in recent years which provide detailed accounts of specific sites and it is to be hoped that many more will yet appear.

Nor is detailed history attempted, dates and outlines being included merely to aid putting the sites into context. Again, various published works deal both with particular quarries and various aspects of the Industry in general.

It cannot be entirely up-to-date as 'landscaping', infill, bulk extraction and decay are constantly changing sites, as is ongoing work at those quarries still operating.

Neither can any claim be made that it is complete, as even the most exhaustive research and fieldwork cannot, with certainty, account for every place where slate may, at some time, have been extracted.

The Gazetteer is, for convenience divided into sections, those in Gwynedd mainly by transport routes, the remainder by geographical regions.

Merfyn Williams,
Ael y Bryn,
Croesor.

WHAT IS SLATE?

Welsh slate is sedimentary rock that due to the action of heat and/or pressure has become grain-orientated so that it readily splits into strong, thin sheets.

Generally Caernarfonshire slate and some in southern Meirionnydd is of the Cambrian series. It is hard and usually of grey-blue colour.

Slate in most of Meirionnydd and southern Dinbych is of the Ordivician series, generally bluer and less brittle than Cambrian.

Slate in northern Dinbych is Silurian, dull grey and less durable.

The Background

Slate has been worked in Wales on a relatively small scale at least since Roman times, mainly for vernacular requirements, but in a few cases for use outside their immediate areas.

It developed as a great industry in the last quarter of the eighteenth century, and aided by the development of transport in what were then remote and primitive areas, expanded more or less continuously throughout the nineteenth century to a peak in the 1890s. A rapid and inexorable decline set in to reach a nadir in the 1960s, with happily something of a rebirth during the 1980s.

Quarrying Methods & the Interpretation of Sites

Slate quarries were (and are) essentially of three basic patterns, dictated by the occurrence and dip of the vein.

1. **Hillside** workings as in the usual stone quarrying manner, either a face or faces on a single level, or in a large quarry by a series of terraces to enable a larger workforce to operate.

2. **Pit workings** where the vein was followed downwards. Where topography permitted, a cutting would be made and/or tunnels bored, to avoid having to uphaul material, and more importantly, waste, and to obviate pumping.

3. **Underground**, where open working would involve the removal of large quantities of overburden, the vein would be reached by tunnelling. It would usually be worked by driving a "roofing shaft" up the top of the vein and working across and downward to develop a chamber. Typically, when a chamber was 70′ wide another would be started leaving an intervening "pillar" some 30-40′ wide to support the roof. This chambering could be repeated on many levels.

Often quarries are a combination of two or three methods. E.g. hillside quarry may have been deepened into a pit and then further exploitation made underground.

At its most basic, slate quarrying consisted of attacking rock exposures to lever out likely blocks. Breaking these blocks into rough rectangles of manageable dimensions, splitting to a thickness suitable for roofing material or for slab and finally trimming to size, exclusively using hand tools, adjacent to the point where the rock was extracted. Or, in the case of underground working, close to the adit.

Quarries might be continuously worked as an established business, supplying a regular market. Or they might be worked as and when a local requirement arose either by the land occupier alongside agriculture as part of the exploitation of his property or by "Slaters" who would dig, make, carry away and roof buildings. Many quarries never progressed beyond this stage and today all that remains is a digging, waste heaps, a working area with possibly the ruins of a shelter and perhaps a track along which finished product was carried away.

Except in the earliest days most quarries used black powder for blasting, to win the rock, using hand drilling for the shot holes. Usually these were bored by a "Jwmpar" slowly and laboriously, by repeated impact. From around 1880 air drills were available, and, earlier and occasionally, hand-powered rotary drills. Mechanically drilled holes can be recognised by the rotation marks.

The absence of shot-hole borings in a working does not imply antiquity as small-scale operations used (and still use) "crowbarring" methods. The larger quarries used high explosive for development work, particularly for tunnelling, and a very few experimented with tunnelling machines. Firesetting was very occasionally used.

Other than some of the most minute workings, there were Walliau or open-fronted dressing sheds, where the work of reduction was carried out. The earlier and smaller sites having them spread singly, adjacent to the working face or in the larger ones, in rows.

Other buildings would include a smithy, for sharpening tools, a powder store, perhaps an office, stabling and almost certainly weighbridges. These latter were mainly used for weighing rubbish to assess "rubblwrs" pay and the presence of them in a very small quarry is evidence of the existence of an employed workforce rather than a friendly partnership. The remoter sites would have barracks for the workforce and possibly cottages that formed almost a village. Many have interesting lavatory structures. Most would have a manager's house (the site recognisable by the trees that invariably screened it).

By the mid 18th C. quarries were using saws to convert the rough blocks into rectangular slab, in place of the "Plwg & Adain", the "Rhys" mallet and other hand methods. These were sandsaws, i.e. bowsaws with no teeth cutting by the action of wet sand in the kerf. Such sawcuts are recognisable by the possibly irregular horizontal cutting marks, and the fact that the saw was not taken right through to the full depth, leaving a rough edge where the slab was broken off. The precise date when sawing was first used is disputed. Handsawn gravestones, dating back almost to the start of the 18th C., have been noted.

Handsawing continued in occasional use until the mid twentieth century, and indeed the hand dividing of large blocks is still carried out.

Water-powered saws were in use by the early 19th C. At first they were merely powered versions of the sand-saw. Often they stood on readily recognisable slab bases and their cuts are more regular than the hand-operated versions, and go right through the slab. They might or might not, be housed in a building.

Circular saws were introduced slightly later and were commonplace by the 1840s, there were originally several types but the industry standard became the moving table, with undertable iron (later steel) blade, based on the timber industry sawbench. The sawmarks are obvious and distinctive. Occasionally in small quarries these were unpowered, being hand cranked by two men.

The other notable circular saw was the fearsome Hunter saw which had an overtable circular blade with inserted, replaceable teeth. Its marks are recognisable by their depth and coarseness of feed.

In the early part of the twentieth century diamond circular saws came into use and have, for some time, been universal. Their blades can be up to over 2 metres in diameter and they exhibit a distinctively fine cut. They invariably have saws moving over a fixed table. (Very occasionally multiple-ganged reciprocating saws have been used.)

Splitting has always remained a hand operation in spite of later attempts to build splitting machines.

Trimming to size was traditionally done by holding the slate over a fixed blade (*Celfi*) and striking it with a knife-like tool (*Cyllell*). Several types of trimming machines were used but the industry standard became the Greaves Rotary Trimmer.

From around 1850 the larger quarries centralised all reduction in an integrated mill, containing the sawing machines, splitting areas and trimming machines, as well as any ancillary machines such as planers and polishers.

The use of mechanical sawing physically separated the winning from the reduction, as the siting of powered machinery was dictated by the availability of water power, and the "gang", normally of four men working a "bargain" became 2 at the face, 2 in the mill. Also, even when stream or electricity provided flexibility of siting, the mill would be at some central point remote from the working face and from tipping areas.

Machines used in integrated mills include,

Saws, usually of the sawmill type, but later, diamond saws.

Trimmers, usually of the Greaves pattern, (usually 1 trimmer per sawbench)

Planers, adapted from the metalworking type but with a blade 10-12″ long.

Sand Polishers, a millstone type polishing head grinds the work surface via a wet sand medium. Still in use in 1990s.

Diamond Polishers, as above but with a much smaller diamond-impregnated head rotating. (A mid 20th C. introduction.)

Gang Saws, very rare.

The latter 4 types only used for producing slab.

In spite of the depredations of scrap-men and collectors, machines or parts of machines, winches, chains, pulleys, pumps, tools and other artifacts may still be found on the remoter sites.

A constant problem was the disposal of waste as only roughly a tenth, or less of the rock extracted became finished product. So that rubbish heaps are the main, and indeed sometimes the only substantial remains on a site. The waste is recognisable as of five types,

1. **Development waste**, consisting of "country rock", often in very large pieces, arising from work needed to reach the slate vein.

2. **Quarrying waste**, irregular pieces of slate discards or trimmings from the working face or from the hand reduction of blocks.

3. **Sawn ends**, found either in dumps or used as building material, which give useful indication of the type and location of saws.

4. **Trimming waste**, fine pieces of slate from the final squaring of roofing slates which indicate that this product was made and where the operation was carried out.

5. **"Fancies"**, pieces that show that ornamental or special shapes were produced.

Water Power

Because of cost, usually only the larger quarries used steam and until the end of the 19th century few had electricity, the almost universal power source being water.

A very few used Pelton wheels or turbines, almost all had waterwheels, basically for driving the saws and other mill machinery, but also, less commonly for winding, pumping, air compressing or even for workshop lathes etc.

Wheels were of 4 types.

Overshot   The most common and most efficient, where water poured forward over the top of the wheel.

Backshot   Slightly less efficient, where the water struck the wheel not quite at the top and rotated it backwards, used where the water supply height did not permit an overshot wheel.

Breastshot   Where, due to even more restricted water-source elevation, the water struck the wheel only about half-way up.

Undershot   Inefficient and rarely used, where due to lack of head the water flowed under the wheel.

The wheelpits, to be seen on so many sites, and the overhead launders (or at least their supporting pillars), their reservoirs and the often extensive and ingenious leat systems both feeding those reservoirs and bringing water to the wheels are usually worthy of study.

Transport

It is railed transport for the Slate Industry that brought about the building of almost all the "Great Little Trains of Wales". Indeed the success of a quarry depended on the availability of good rail transport. These well known lines were fed by feeders from quarries, which in themselves make interesting objects of study.

In addition the use of some kind of rails was almost universal for movement within the site itself, normally 2'g (or thereabouts) with 3 main kinds of truck. Open fronted rubbish wagons both to convey rubble from the quarry and trimmings and sawn ends to the tip. Flat wagons for carrying blocks to the mill and fence-sided trucks for finished product. Wagons or fragments of wagons are discoverable on many sites.

Rail tracks, or at least the formations that carried them, can show how, from the quarrying faces, blocks were conveyed to the mill, and waste to the rubbish runs. Also, how waste from the mill was taken to mill waste tips and finished product to the stocking yard, and finally, off site or to a loading point. Variations in level usually involved inclines, and drumhouse and incline formations are a characteristic of all but the smallest sites. Many have part, or in some cases, all of the machinery virtually intact. The variation in construction of these inclines and drumhouses makes a fascinating study in itself.

Those, usually smaller quarries, that had, or originally had, no external rail connection, often have most elaborately engineered tracks. Sometimes intended for carts, but often steep, narrow tracks only passable by pack-animals.

Site Visits

A few quarries are open to the public so access is no problem. Often the serious visitor, on making his interest known may be taken to parts not normally on view.

Owing to insurance constraints, entering working quarries is not possible but prior application may result in a conducted visit being arranged. As regards the majority of sites, though they are abandoned, they are still private property so permission of the owner *must always be obtained*. If access is only possible by departing from public rights of way,

14

permission to cross private land must also be obtained. Such permissions are usually freely given once it is established that ones interest is serious, that one abides by the Country Code and that one has no dog.

For visiting remote sites, the usual precautions for mountain walking apply — suitable clothing and footwear, spare clothing, compass, whistle, map, food and an up-to-date weather forecast.

Do not scorn the small sites, pathetic little scratchings though they may be. Each one represents toil and dedication, hope and disappointment, hardship, disease and early death, endured for scant reward.

All sites are dangerous. Slate waste is slippery when even only slightly wet, rockfalls are prevalent, buildings are generally unsafe and concealed shafts and openings may be unguarded.

Going underground is particularly hazardous. Three persons is the minimum desirable party, one, experienced in mine exploration, being designated leader, who must brief any inexperienced members of the party before entering. This leader should be first in and last out. If the party numbers more than about six, another experienced person should be nominated deputy leader.

Either wear rubber knee-boots or be prepared for wet feet, wear a light, brightly coloured waterproof. In winter be prepared for apparent warmth inside, and in summer the reverse. Hard hats *must* be worn, it is desirable to carry a stick for testing ground and water depth. One person should have a rope.

Lights should be substantial handlamps or caplamps (with new batteries) with a reserve torch or two among the party.

Be sure someone, not going underground, knows where you are. It is wise to leave something such as a rucksack at the entrance you use.

Once underground, pause to allow your eyes to accommodate. Always examine the roof as you proceed. Any areas of new-looking fallen rock should be avoided. Beware of shafts leading to lower workings, particularly if walking in water. One should never stand on timber. In strange, complex workings, operate a "keep left" rule and memorise "landmarks". Keep together and immediately follow the leaders instructions.

Never remove anything from a site, if an artifact is moved or uncovered for examination or photography, replace and recover it.

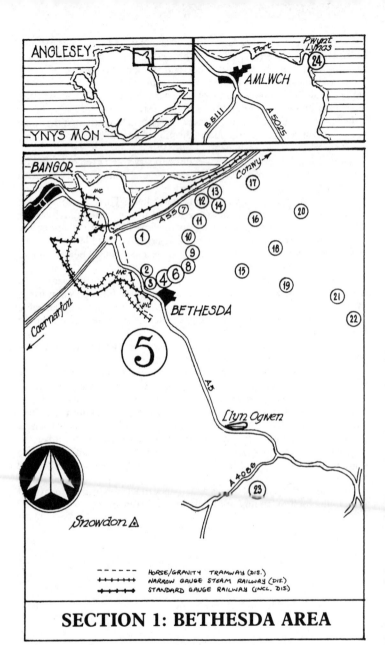

ANGLESEY

YNYS MÔN

Port

AMLWCH

Pwynt
Lynas

B5111 · A5025 · 24

BANGOR

Conwy

A55 · 7 · 12 · 13 · 14 · 11 · 17 · 16 · 20

inc

1 · 10 · 9 · 8 · 18 · 15 · 19 · 21 · 22

2 · 3 · 4 · 6

inc

inc

BETHESDA

Caernarfon

5

A5

Llyn Ogwen

A4086 · 23

Snowdon ▲

- - - - -   HORSE/GRAVITY TRAMWAY (DIS.)
+++++++   NARROW GAUGE STEAM RAILWAY (DIS.)
++++++   STANDARD GAUGE RAILWAY (INCL. DIS.)

SECTION 1: BETHESDA AREA

Caernarfon, Bethesda Area Section 1
Plus Anglesey, Ynys Môn

General

This section covers the Ogwen valley, and is centred around the village of Bethesda. The slate is of the Cambrian series.

The area is entirely dominated by the Penrhyn Quarry, as was (and is) the whole Welsh Slate Industry. Typically throughout its existence that quarry has supplied a quarter and more of the total Welsh output. Abundant, excellent rock of near vertical dip being worked by open terracing on the flanks of Mynydd Elidir.

Since it is a working quarry archaeological remains are constantly vanishing as modern work advances, but if permission can be obtained to visit, there is much to be seen, and on a scale that, Dinorwig apart, is not found elsewhere.

The other quarries, situated to the North East of the Ogwen valley, off Penrhyn land, were, with three or four exceptions, extremely small and emphemeral affairs. They were mainly open hillside workings although a few, unusually for this area, went underground. Some were made viable by the occurrence of coloured (red & green) material, and some prospered briefly during the 1900-1903 and other Penrhyn disputes. Only about three have remains of any great significance.

Transport

The Penrhyn quarry proprietors made considerable road improvements towards the end of the 18th C. to facilitate cartage to the mouth of the river Ogwen and afterwards to the purpose built Port Penrhyn.

In 1801 a horse-drawn 2'g. railway was built linking Penrhyn quarry with Port Penrhyn. This was the first and possibly best of several such lines which so dramatically reduced the cost of transporting slate from quarry to the port. The civil work was good and the three inclines evenly spread facilitated efficient working. Although the original round bar rail and semicircular wheel profile was unsuccessful, relaid on conventional rail it served the quarry for 75 years finally carrying daily tonnages far in excess of its designed capacity.

It left the Coed y Parc area to cross a minor road on the level at SH614666 from where it can be walked (traces of slate sleepers) to the head of the Gilgeraint incline. From here there is little trace for several miles other than the head of an archway where the Dinas incline went under a minor road at SH607685. Close to the Llandegai roundabout a lane defines the route which is from there on lost under the Llandegai Industrial Estate. The passage under the main road at SH594714 is still open. From there the route is defined by the curved wall of the Penrhyn Castle estate. At the head of the Marchogion incline the drumhouse and stables are in re-use as a dwelling. Near the foot of that incline there is a single arched bridge over the river Cegin, the route then passes under the later steam railway (see below) to recross the Cegin by a fine three-arched bridge and so on to Port Penrhyn.

In 1876 this line was replaced by a steam railway (also 2' nominal g.) that operated until 1962.

This left Coed y Parc by a similar route but at a higher level, the slate embankment being still extant. The route is readily traceable curving around Tregarth, virtually interlacing the Standard Gauge line. The viaduct at Felin-hen has vanished and beyond there the track is much overgrown. From near Maesgeirchen, where it passed under the main road, it is clearly defined to the nice little span over the track of the old tramway and on to the steel and wood bridge over the Cegin which it shared with the Standard Gauge, (Port Penrhyn branch), and on via an arch (now blocked) to the dockside. The Port Penrhyn branch of the L&NWR opened in 1852 (closed 1963) enabled transfer onto rail of slate brought to Port Penrhyn by the Penrhyn Railway. It is readily traceable including the bridge across the Cegin which was later widened on its south-eastern side to share with the Penrhyn steam line.

It is of note that of the original 1801 horse-drawn Penrhyn line, the section from the port to beyond the top of the Marchogion incline took over the works of an earlier tramway (not used for slate). This passed through what is now Llandegai village to an incline down to the mouth of the river Ogwen. This incline (severed by the L&NWR main line) is traceable.

The port itself, remains relatively undisturbed, apart from the lifting of track. There are several buildings of interest, including the writing slate factory, an engine shed, offices and a unique, circular lavatory.

Other than Penrhyn, the quarries carted to Bangor, although after the Bethesda branch of the L&NWR opened in 1884, rail transport was available to them. Much of this branch, which closed in 1963, is readily traceable to its junction with the main line near Llandegai.

Anglesey, Ynys Môn

For convenience, the one quarry in Anglesey, Llaneilian, is included in this section it is notable for the spectactular steps cut into the cliff-face.

1.	SH611696	Chwarel Las
2.	613677	Dolgoch
3.	617673	Coed
4.	619672	Coetmor

5.	620650	Penrhyn
6.	623671	Pant Dreiniog
7.	624704	Bronydd Isaf
8.	626678	Moelfaban
9.	628679	Ty'n Ffridd
10.	628683	Tan y Bwlch
11.	631693	Bryn Hafod y Wern
12.	632706	Bronydd
13.	635707	Ffridd
14.	636701	Dolpistyll
15.	642672	Dr Hughes
16.	642697	Cwm Glas
17.	645708	Crymlyn
18.	649680	Gallt y Mawn
19.	652668	Afon Gaseg
20.	657698	Pant y Darren
21.	678663	Afon Wen
22.	683655	Cwm Bychan
23.	688561 & 686560	Cwm Clorod
24.	481932	Llaneilian

AFON GAM = Pant y Darren

AFON GASEG SH652668
Underground.
A very tiny working.
Remains Collapsed adit, some rubbish runs and traces of access track.
Also excavation at 647668. (19)

AFON WEN SH678663
Small working
Remains Excavation only. (21)

BRACHIA Possibly Pant y Darren

BRONYDD SH632706
Putative site.
Remains Small pit. (12)

BRONYDD ISAF SH624704
Possible trial.
Remains Possible ground disturbance. (7)

BRYN HAFOD Y WERN SH631693
Pit.

Owing to unavailability of land downhill, the pit could not be made self-draining and all material had to be up-hauled to the mill and waste further uphauled to lengthy tipping runs. Also the need to re-use a limited water supply (which had to be brought from Llyn Caseg) meant a less than ideal layout of the mill area.

Established around 1780, it was operated by the Pennants, but abandoned by them in 1845, probably due to excessive working costs. Re-opened by the Royal Bangor Slate Co. in 1845 (who in due course built the mills). It was closed in 1884 when the Pennants cut off the water supply.

Rock was raised from the 200′ deep pit to a landing platform by a water powered incline, which may have replaced an earlier water balance (the same wheel also pumping) rubbish being further raised to the rubbish runs by another water powered incline, whose tailrace supplied the first haulage.

Good slate was lowered from the landing platform by a short self acting incline to a small mill, with a further similar incline to a second, lower mill. The mill wheels being driven in tandem from water from the haulages. Thus water was four times used. It is not known how pumping was powered but this may have been by water wheel also. Product was carted to Bangor for shipment.

In 1882, shortly before closure output was 2198 tons pa with 65 men employed, probably about half the scale of a decade before.

Remains The pit is now filled with water and the buildings are ruinous but it is relatively undisturbed. The foundations of buildings, incline formations and tramway layout are clear. The financial constraints are shown by the traces of wagons having run on slate ways. There is a pleasing pointed arch providing access to the upper mills area under the landing platform, Bryn Hall, the owner's house has a fine arched entrance gate and is still in occupation.

The long leat from the river Caseg to the two reservoirs may be traced, and the launder pillars and underground supply relief pipe are prominent. (11)

CAE DRAICH Y CAFN
Pre 1782 site of several diggings under Take Notes, which became Penrhyn Quarry.

CHWAREL LAS SH611696
Pit, very small.
Remains Rubbish runs only. (1)

CHWAREL PARRY Original name of Gallt y Mawn.

CILFODEN = Pandreiniog

CLODDFA Y COED = Coed

COED SH617673
Hillside quarry, very small.
Remains Building ruins possibly associated with quarry. (3)

COED UCHA = Cloddfa y Coed

COED Y DDOL = Ddol Goch

COETMOR SH619672 Adjacent to Pantdreiniog, used by latter for tipping after 1870s
No remains. (4)

CRYMLYN SH645708
Hillside pit, extremely small.
Remains Excavation, some rubbish, small building possibly associated. Much use in locality of fencing etc., handworked. (17)

CWM BYCHAN SH683655
Small, possibly not slate.
Remains Excavation only. (22)

CWM CLOROD SH688561 & 686560
Possible trial.
Remains Slight excavations only. (23)

CWM GLAS SH642697
Pit, very small, circa 1890.
Remains Only a hole in hillside. (16)

DOLAWEN Early name for part of Penrhyn.

DOLGOCH SH613677
Smallpit, operated for few years after 1836.
Remains Depression in ground. (2)

DOLPISTYLL SH636701
Pit, very small.
Remains Rubbish runs and some building vestiges. (14)

FFRIDD SH635707
Putative quarry.
Remains Possible ground disturbance. (13)

FFRIDD FEDW Possible alternative name Dolpistyll.

FRONLLWYD One of the Take Note workings incorporated in Penrhyn in 1785.

GALLT Y MAWN SH649680
Pit.
Very small, worked occasionally from about 1865, possibly slightly larger than the other tiny workings in this area.
Remains Two small slits in ground. (18)

DR HUGHES SH642672
Open quarry, very small.
Remains Small pit. (15)

LLIDIART-Y-GRAIANYN Possibly Dr Hughes.

LLEWELLYN Possibly Cwm Glas.

MOELFABAN SH626678
Underground.
A small quarry producing speciality slate, opened in mid 19th C.
Adits, on three levels with incline connection, generally little chambering, good rock, red at first, then green coming from tunnels.
Like Tan-y-Bwlch and Pant Dreiniog, was operated co-operatively during the 1900-03 stoppage.
Originally material was lowered by a second incline, possibly to a small mill, and carted out via Rachub village, but later a tramway connection may have been made to Tan-y-Bwlch quarry mill. Closed early 1900's.
Remains Little other than the adits, (two penetrable for a short distance), some traces of buildings, the impressive grass covered upper incline formation and, nearby a nice row of cottages. (8)

MOEL WNION Possibly this is Cwm Glas.

PANT DREINIOG SH623671
Pit/Underground.
Opened around 1850. Steam & locos at one time employed, records of a water balance also, closed in 1911 after having been co-operatively run. Unsuccessfully re-opened in 1920s to produce slate powder. Output cannot have exceed a few hundreds of tons pa. (245 tons, 13 men in 1882).
No remains Site entirely landscaped, but housing to the North East of the site is of interest. (6)

PANT Y DARREN SH657698
Pit.
Doubtful if any saleable product was ever actually won.
Remains Digging could be run-in adit. (20)

PENRHYN SH620650

Terraced hillside quarry (some pit working).

Originally worked in 16th C. Present undertaking dates from 1782 when Richard Pennant bought out the existing leases. Within 10 years its 5 figure tonnages pa dominated the industry and by the latter part of the 19th C. tonnages of around 100,000 pa were routinely produced. (In 1882 11166 tons with 2089 men.) Apart from Dinorwig, it was several times the size of any other quarry.

By 1798 the problem of enabling a large number of men to work simultaneously was solved by the gallery system whereby the working face was terraced out at 65'/70' intervals. Ultimately there were 21 such galleries, each with its own rail system. Movement downwards was mainly by self-acting incline and upwards by water balance lifts, of a unique type. Latterly some use was made of aerial ropeways. There was, and still is, some pit working.

Originally all dressing was done by hand on the galleries, machine sawing was introduced in the 1830s and by the 1850s work was centred in several large mills, water, steam and latterly electric powered. As was usual in Caernarfonshire machine trimming came late and never was widespread as in, say Ffestiniog, so that there were virtually streets of wallia for hand dressing adjacent to the mills. Contrasting with practice at Dinorwig and elsewhere where hand trimming was carried out in bays in the mills themselves.

Steam locomotives were introduced in 1876, and i.c. power in the 1930s, all locos were replaced by lorries by 1964.

There was extensive electrification in the early 20th C.

Prior to the establishment of Port Penrhyn, as a harbour and a site for a writing slate factory and other "downstream" activities in 1790, slate was carted to Bangor for shipment.

In 1801 the horse/gravity Penrhyn tramroad replaced the 140 men and 400 waggons by then employed in cartage. This tramway was in turn replaced by the steam hauled Penrhyn Railway in 1878.

After the opening in 1852 of the Main Line, Port Penrhyn branch, an increasing tonnage was transferred to rail instead of being shipped coastwise.

Quarrying still continues at the lower levels only, with all movement being by lorry, fork truck and conveyor. The present mill is new but a number of old buildings, notably the office continue in reuse.

Remains Although the lower workings are much disturbed by modern bulk working and by road construction much of the upper workings, to the S, are in remarkably good state. There are a number of inclines and drumhouses, including some with horizontal sheave gear and a nice powered incline with sheaves and cable ducts. There are numerous buildings including mills, engine sheds etc., and several extensive rakes of dressing sheds. The precipitous terraces are a notable feature. There is much rail, pointwork and other artifacts on the ground.

There is a virtually complete electric ropeway with wooden towers and also an almost complete steel pyloned Blondin.

One of the water balance lifts is preserved near the main office and there is at least one other on site.

The present mills, built on the site of the old Red Lion mill are equipped with the latest diamond saws and have splitting machines although much hand splitting is still done. Belt conveyors are much used.

At Coed y Parc, (615663) which was a concentrated industrial complex, there are several buildings in fair condition including two housing waterwheels fed by inverted syphons. This was the terminus of both the Penrhyn tramway and the later Penrhyn railway and apart from workshops etc. there were mills, the first dating from 1803. On the other side of the road the Ogwen Tile Works, later a slate mill, is now in industrial reuse.

On the hillside above and to the west is an extensive water supply layout. There are many items of peripheral interest in the area, such as paths, steps, stiles, cottages (with long allotment like gardens) and the model village of Llandegai.

(Continuing extraction has obliterated much of the upper part of the site, including the blondins etc.). (5)

TAN Y BWLCH SH628683

Pit/underground.

Established around 1805 it continued in sporadic use, including a period as a co-operative, until 1911.

Rock was uphauled from a pit and reduced in a small mill. Later some underground working from the pit with vertical shaft haulage. Two steam engines used. A constricted site made tipping a problem. Stated to have had a drainage level emerging near Llanllechid church. Tonnage unlikely to have exceeded about 500 pa.

Material originally carted but latterly a possible connection to the Moelfaban incline.

Remains some buildings, (in reuse) one with a slate sign "Bangor Slate Co", much tipping, tightly squeezed into a restricted space, there are the abutments of two rubbish run bridges and a stack of finished product on the stockyard.

The pit is partly run-in obliterating any adits and any uphaulage arrangements. There is an unusually large engine house with an adjacent shaft (filled) some 4 x 4 m, stone lined. Presumably for uphaulage but run-off arrangements unclear. It is not obvious where second engine, presumably for saw power, was sited. (10)

TY'N FFRIDD SH628679

Hillside/Underground.

Very small, operated in early 19th C.
Remains Virtually none. (9)

Y FOEL Alternative name for all or part of Moelfaban.

Anglesey

LLANEILIAN SH481932
A spectacular series of cliff face workings.
Remains Small working faces, some buildings, traces of access track. The notable feature is a most extraordinary flight of steps cut into the cliff to give access from the sea. There is some indication that an attempt was made to go underground. (24)

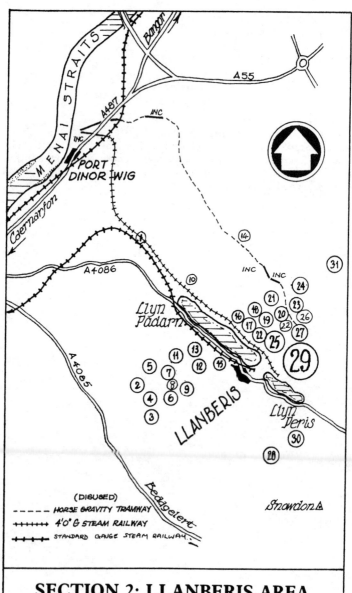

MENAI STRAITS

Bangor

A55

A487

INC

PORT DINOR WIG

Caernarfon

INC

A4086

14

INC   INC

31

10

24

21

23

Llyn Padarn

16   18   20   26

17   19   22   27

22   25

13

11   12   15   29

5

7

2   8   9

4   6

3   LLANBERIS

Llyn Peris

30

28

(DISUSED)

- - - - HORSE GRAVITY TRAMWAY

+++++ 4'0" G STEAM RAILWAY

+++ STANDARD GAUGE STEAM RAILWAY

Beddgelert

Snowdon ▲

SECTION 2: LLANBERIS AREA

Caernarfon, Llanberis Area Section 2

General

This area of Cambrian Series was workable both to the north east and the south west of the Valley. As at Bethesda the area is dominated by one quarry, the Dinorwig which worked the southern flank of Mynydd Elidir. Part of the Dinorwig/Vivians complex is readily accessible as a Country Park. The rest is the property of Nuclear Power as it is the site of the Dinorwig Pumped Storage Scheme. Taken together both the public part and (if permission to visit is obtained) the N.P. enclosure, together with the North Wales Quarrying Museum, represent the largest concentration of artifacts to be seen anywhere in the industry.

On the same side of the valley, are several very minor quarries, only one, Vaynol, being more than a tiny scratching.

On the opposite side of the valley are a number of sites, some very small but others, though dwarfed by Dinorwig, were quite substantial undertakings.

Transport

As at Bethesda the dominant quarry was served by its own private railway and specially constructed port.

The first line was the 1824 2'g. Dinorwig tramway. This left the quarry halfway up the present site, the first part of the route being lost in subsequent workings. It continued on the line of the present public road which runs through Dinorwig village (making partial use of the foundations of the earlier 'Village tramway') to the head of the Upper Cwm incline at SH579624. This is now a steep footpath which continues via a manoeuvring loop down the Lower Cwm incline to stables at the lower part of Deiniolen. Its route towards Clwt-y-bont is defined by present streets before it swings right across fields. At SH565656 is the rebuilt smithy/stables which served the line (and which continued as a smithy until about 1930). The line is lost beyond here but can be traced where it swings right off the B4547 and is defined by a line through trees to the head of the Garth incline near Garth Fach farm. The incline is largely lost in forestry but slate sleepers can be found. The line is again lost by roadworks and the construction of the L&NWR but the western portal of the tunnel which carried it under the A487 is visible in a field. The short stretch into Port Dinorwig is obvious if not actually traceable.

Unlike the Penrhyn horse line of 1801 this line did not start at the lowest point of quarry working so uphauling was required and the fall of the line was much greater. The civil work was of questionable quality, the uneven spacing of the inclines hampered efficient working, the gradients were variable and the use of slate sleepers caused maintenance problems. After only a few years complete replacement was called for.

The new line, the Padarn railway, although not originally steamed, was laid out in 1842 for steam operation. In view of the limited power, and the constriction of minimum size of locomotives then available, it was almost level with one incline and built to the unusual gauge of 4'.

It ran from a terminus at Gilfach Ddu, (where the 2'g. quarry wagons were loaded in fours onto carrier trucks). It ran alongside Llyn Padarn, passing the miniscule Ladas and Boundary quarries and, via a curve (later straightened), past the foot of the Vaynol quarry incline. The trackbed is now reused by the Llanberis Lake Railway. At Brynrefail the trackbed briefly becomes a road before passing under a road bridge, continuing on as a footpath to Pontrhythallt where there is an engine shed. It again passes under a road from where, it runs alongside the formation of the standard gauge, Llanberis branch. Between the two lines are the long, narrow sites of the Crawia and Pontrhythallt slate works.

The trackbed again passes under a road and swings right near Penrhyn farm. It may be followed with varying difficulty to a footbridge with high clearance to suit the original locomotives (one of which, together with some quarry artifacts, is displayed in Penrhyn Castle). Nearby is a fine carriage shed, for workmens' train stock.

The B4366 was crossed on the level at Saron and after a mile the formation swings left under a byroad to become a lane where there are railway cottages still in occupation. This lane leads to the large drumhouse/unloading shed at the head of the Penscoins incline. There is an engine/carriage shed, further railway housing, still occupied and a nice little hut partly constructed of stone sleeper blocks, one of several examples, on the route, where such blocks have been used for constructional purposes.

From this drumhouse wagons were lowered by chain, down the 2'g. incline to Port Dinorwig. There are vestiges of the original underfloor sheave arrangements as well as the conventional drum which replaced them in the 1920s.

The portal of the, now blocked, tunnel where the wagons emerged at Port Dinorwig quayside can be seen.

Although during the 1840s and 50s this railway conferred a competitive advantage on Dinorwig quarry, the trouble of loading and unloading wagons and crewling them down to the port became increasingly burdensome right up to the 1962 closure.

As at Port Penrhyn there was a branch of the L&NWR to Port Dinworig to enable slate brought down the Padarn line to be trans-shipped to the main line system. Opened 1857 closed 1960, some of the trackbed is traceable.

Although marred by marina development the fine little port area is largely unaltered, apart from the lifting of track. Several buildings are in reuse including the dry-dock workshops.

Being both a private line and the wrong side of the valley, the Padarn railway could not be used by the quarries on the southern side, and they had to cart to Caernarfon, the lower ones via Llanrug, the upper ones via Wernfawr.

This dramatically changed after 1869 when the L&NWR standard gauge Llanberis branch opened. Either direct or via the extended Ffridd incline system, almost all the quarries could connect to the railway yard at Llanberis. This enabled the quarries to either use the national rail network, or have access to the slate quays at Caernarfon.

This standard gauge line, closed in 1964 now partly reused for road improvements, makes a pleasant walk alongside Llyn Padarn, passing under a pretty accommodation bridge. Much of the rest of the route is readily traceable to its junction to the south west of Caernarfon.

1.	SH536643 & 540641	Crawia (works)
2.	552600	Chwarel Fawr
3.	553597	Donnen Las
4.	555595	Brynmawr
5.	555604	Cefn Du
6.	557598	Bwlch y Groes
7.	560605	Cook & Ddol
8.	561602	Twll Goch
9.	562601	Caermeinciau
10.	563622	Pen Llyn
11.	565607	Glynrhonwy Upper
12.	566603	Cambrian
13.	570610	Glynrhonwy Lower
14.	572632	Clwt y Bont (works)
15.	572606	Goodmans
16.	575614	Boundary
17.	578610	Ladas
18.	578615	Vaynol
19.	579613	Chwarel Isaf
20.	579617	Fronhyfryd
21.	581617	Chwarel Goch
22.	582607	Alltwen
23.	582619	Lloc
24.	584619	Frondirion
25.	586605	Vivian
26.	589616	Chwarel Fawr
27.	591610	Allt Ddu
28.	594576	Arddu
29.	595603	Dinorwig

| 30. | 601583 | Gallt y Llan |
| 31. | 602628 | Marchlyn |

ADELAIDE
South part of Allt Ddu.

ALLT DDU SH591610
Pit/hillside working. Operating prior to 1771, in 1809 absorbed into Dinorwig, but operated as a separate department in conjunction with Chwarel Fawr. The mill was not used after 1870, all material being railed to the adjacent Dinorwig mill.
Remains The main excavation to the east of the road and the substantial mills area with buildings, inclines (including an interesting transporter incline) and extensive rubbish runs to the west of the road, have been completely landscaped. (27)

ALLTWEN SH582607
Putative site.
Remains In trees, possible ground disturbance. (22)

ARDDU SH594576
Open quarry.
A tiny undertaking consisting of two tandem cuts.
Remains Ruins of a dressing shed and other small buildings on upper level. The stocking area has several thousand finished slates, mainly doubles and small doubles and parts of a rubbish truck. (28)

BOUNDARY SH575614
An ancient small open working on the lakeside. Site of an early loading point.
Remains Tiny dressing shed against rock face. (16)

BRAICH
An early Dinorwig working, near the present eastern extremity of site. Name later given to SE part of complex.

BRYNGLAS
Close to Adelaide. Operating prior to 1771 absorbed into Dinorwig in 1809.

BRYNHYFRYD = Fron Hyfryd

BRYN LLYS
Old quarry forming part of Dinorwig.

BRYNMAWR SH555595
Open quarry/pit.
Very small, operated intermittently in the 1860s and 1880s. Taken over
by Cefn Du in 1886. Steam was used for pumping and hauling. Product
was carried by tramway to the head of the Cefn Du incline. Output only a
few hundred tons pa. (1883 160 tons).
Remains Virtually nothing other than the pit itself, some rubbish runs, the
tramway formation and the steam powered incline. (4)

BWLCH Y GROES SH557598
Open quarry/pit.
Small, operated in the 18th C. Revived during 1870s. Taken over by Cefn
Du in 1886. Product carried by tramway to the head of the Cefn Du
Incline. Output of a few hundred tons pa.
Remains A surprisingly large pit with rubbish runs and a very degraded
tramway formation. Ruins of a barrack building to the west. (6)

CAERMEINCIAU SH562601
Open Quarry.
A small and entirely unmechanised quarry operated in 1870s and 1880s,
on the site of a much earlier undertaking. No railed access, may have
carted to Ffridd incline. (1883 300 tons, 12 men)
Remains Almost none, other than rubbish runs overlying much earlier
rubbish runs. (9)

CAMBRIAN SH566603
Open quarry/pit.
A hotch potch of small workings, operating from the mid 19th C. in
conjunction with Goodmans, both amalgamating with Cefn Du in 1878.
There was a tramway connection to the Ffridd incline. Output around
1000 tons pa.
Remains Pits, a network of tramway formations and rubbish runs and
several collapsed tunnels. Some ruins of small buildings and a possible
mill (Steam? powered). One pit clearly produced red slate. The Ffridd
incline was single acting with a steam haulage that replaced an earlier
water turbine. (12)

CEFN DU SH555604
Open quarry/pit.
Opened in the late 18th C. Closed 1928. Consisted of several pits, with a
tramway system basically on 2 levels, the upper one having tunnels to
connect the various districts and connected by an incline to the lower
level, which was in turn itself connected by an incline to the mills area.
After amalgamation with Chwarel Fawr, material was brought from
there, via a tunnel for reduction in the Cefn Du mills.

By 1879 there were said to be 4 steam engines, 2 waterwheels and a water turbine on the site. Latterly electric power was used. Locomotives were employed. Originally product was carted to Caernarfon via Groeslon, but after amalgamation with Goodman & Cambrian in 1878 the Ffridd incline was extended by 2 self acting pitches and a tramway connection made to its head. A substantial undertaking with an output (including associated quarries) of 5640 tons with 197 men in 1882.

Remains The pits and tunnels are much collapsed, there are several ruined buildings in the mills area including a large, roofless, but otherwise well preserved mill. The rubbish tips make a spectacular landscape feature. (5)

COED Y DDOL Part of Goodmans.

CHWAREL BACH Early part of Glynrhonwy.

CHWAREL COOK Early part of Cook and Ddol.

CHWAREL FAIN
Early development on Glynrhonwy Upper Site.

CHWAREL FAWR SH552600
Pit.

The uppermost of the contiguous line of quarries on the northern slope of Moel Eilio. In spite of its name it was not a large undertaking, indeed, until the late 1860s was very small. Material was originally carted to Caernarfon, via Waunfawr. Later it was connected by a tramway to the Ffridd incline but after amalgamation with Cefn Du in 1883, this line was abandoned, material being taken by tunnel to this latter quarry for reduction. This tunnel also served as a drain enabling deeper working.

Remains A crater-like pit with rubbish piled up almost all around it. The tunnel which carried the tramway to the incline head is open and the tramway route readily traceable. (There is a stock of slates alongside the tram route but this is likely to be from later reworking.) There are no buildings, possibly there were some in the pit area but they disappeared when the working was deepened after the Cefn Du take over. The entrance to the Cefn Du tunnel is visible and there is a collapsed tunnel which carried a rubbish run. There are vestiges of a short incline possibly associated with early workings. There are traces of an apparent tramway connection to Brynmawr quarry. (2)

CHWAREL FAWR SH589616
Not to be confused with above, it was part of the Dinorwig complex. Operated in conjunction with Allt Ddu, approached by an adit under the road.

Remains Virtually only the excavation, landscaped.

N.B. This name was early applied to part of Vivian. (26)

CHWAREL FAWNOG An early development on the Glynrhonwy Lower site.

CHWAREL GOCH SH581617
Hillside working, larger than others nearby.
Remains Pit to north of road, accessed by two tunnels (blocked), tips to south of road on several levels. Buildings adapted and in reuse as dwellings. (21)

CHWAREL GRIFFITH ELLIS = Allt Ddu.

CHWAREL HIR Also Chwarel Huw Dafydd, Chwarel Morgan, Chwarel Owen, Chwarel y Maen, Chwarel y Pigia. Early diggings of Cefn Du/Chwarel Fawr.

CHWAREL HIR This name was also applied to early diggings at Glynrhonwy.

CHWAREL ISAF SH579613
Pit working, connected to Vaynol by tramway.
Remains Tramway formation, drainage tunnel. (19)

CHWAREL ISAF This name also applied to early diggings at Glynrhonwy.

CHWAREL MYNYDD
One of the late 18th C. quarries that became part of Dinorwig.

CHWAREL Y PERSON = Goodmans.

CLODDFA GRIFFITH ELLIS Early name for (part of) Allt Ddu.

CLODDFA Y FFORD Early part of Glynrhonwy.

CLOGWEN Y GIGFRAN Early quarry absorbed into Wellington.

COOK & DDOL SH560605
Pit.
Operated intermittently from early 19th C. one of the few in the immediate area to have a mill. Material carted from the west of the site up to time of building of Ffridd incline. Connection being made to the original head of incline by a short self acting incline, later by a tunnel. After the Ffridd was extended access was via the head of the lower pitch of the extension.
Output is unlikely to have exceeded 1000 tons pa. (631 tons with 26 men in 1882). Closed early 20th C.

Remains The pit is divided by a causeway to give access to Ffridd incline. There is a large, ruinous mill and other buildings. At a lower level is a large working area served by a tunnel from the pit and a possible uphaulage incline to the mill above. There is an interesting building alongside the Ffridd incline which has a heavy slabbed roof and a fine fireplace. There are extensive rubbish runs and vestiges of some tunnels. (7)

CLOGWYN Y GIGFRAN
Early Dinorwig quarry possibly near Main (Village) Mills.

CLWT Y BONT SH572632
Slate mill A large multi-storey building, served by Dinorwig Tramway? *Remains* Building in reuse, with waterwheel still in situ inside. (14)

CRAWIA/PONTRHYTHALLT SH540641/536643
Slate Works.

Three works sited on a narrow strip between the Padarn & L&NWR lines. Operated from 1880s to 1920s processing slate into writing slates and slab products from Dinorwig material brought to the eastern end of the site on the Padarn Railway. Water powered in tandem, the shallow fall of ground, forced the wide separation of the works. Finished product was loaded onto a L&NWR siding.

Remains At the eastern end some vestiges of buildings, one with a waterwheel axle. At the western end, several buildings are in reuse including a house and a mill converted into a dwelling. Most of the leat is traceable and some of the tramway which connected the works with each other and with the railway siding. (1)

DINORWIG SH595603
Hillside Terraces.

Established in 1787 when a group headed by landowner Assheton-Smith took over the pre-existing Take Note workings.

By the end of that century operations were consolidated into a series (ultimately 13) of terraces each 60'/75' high. Although the first incline was built in 1789, sledge operations continued until 1816, after which all downhill movement was by self-acting inclines, there eventually being 2 main incline systems, each consisting of many pitches. An unusual feature of Dinorwig inclines was the practice of one pitch connecting not 2, but 3 terraces, traffic from the intermediate terrace being hitched and unhitched "on the run".

From the 1830s there was a tramway system on each terrace, laid out so that material was generally conveyed in one direction to the incline and in the other direction to the tipping area, efforts being made to slant the terraces slightly to facilitate movement. Steam locomotives were introduced onto the terraces in the 1870s, and petrol locos in the 1930s. At one time track mileage was said to exceed 50 and compressed air piping to exceed 15 miles.

Several Blondins were installed also in the 1930s.

From the mid 19th C. central mill working was used, the main mills area for the north-western side was on "Mills Level" at the same height as Dinorwig village but there were numerous mills at various points on the site. Extensive use was made of both water and steam power, in 1905 electricity from Cwm Dyli was laid on.

Early transport was by boat along Llyn Padarn then by cart to the coast. (There are suggestions, but no evidence of an early tramway alongside the lake.) Although Port Dinorwic was built in 1793, and some roads laid, it was not until 1824 that the Dinorwig Tramway to it was built. This tramway quickly proved unsatisfactory and in 1842 was replaced by the Padarn Railway. Part of the route of the early tramway was later rebuilt as a locomotive line to dispose of waste from the main mills area and to connect with Alltddu and Chwarel Fawr quarries.

The Padarn line, steamed in 1848, continued in use until 1961.

The eventual scale of this quarry was such that its output of around 100,000 tons pa in the late 1890s, (87429 tons with 2757 men in 1882) was on a par with Penrhyn, and represented almost a quarter of the total output of Welsh Slate.

Finally closed 1969.

Remains There is a great deal on this vast site and although much is no longer accessible, some of the western part and the whole of the Vivian quarry (separate from, but operated in conjunction with the main complex) is open to the public. The CEGB pumped storage scheme has destroyed the area of Wellington mill and the workings and lower C series inclines in that vicinity, and there has been some work and tipping on the upper part of the site, but generally CEGB occupation has ensured survival of many artifacts.

The workshops building at Gilfach Ddu houses the North Wales Quarrying Museum, apart from a unique display of artifacts and relics, there is the big water wheel and the turbine that supplanted it.

Nearby is the entrance to the Glan y Bala tunnel which provided a connection to the south-eastern area, until tipping enabled the line to be relaid around the bluff. This tunnel is now in reuse as a cable route.

On the hillside is the hospital building (open as a museum) and behind can be traced the embankment of an abortive rail line. Adjacent is the arched entrance to Vivian quarry. A path partly incorporating steps made from slate sleepers climbs alongside Vivian to Dinorwig village.

In the woods above is a large powder house.

Behind and above Vivian quarry, near the end of the public road out from Dinorwig village were Chwarel Fawr and Allt Ddu quarries. This public road defines the route of the 1824 Tramway. The private road which continues towards the main mills defines the later Village loco line, which connected these quarries to the main complex and also served as an outlet for rubbish for tipping.

The main quarry was divided into 2 sides, the NW known as Garret, comprised (successively down from the top): Alice, Llangristiolus, Aberdaron, Lernion, Twll Mwg, Bonc Roller, Swallow, Tophet, Abbysinia, Twll Dwnclwr, Penrhydd Bach, Penrhydd, Sinc Penrhydd, Sinc Twll Clawdd, Mills/Village, Harriet, California, Pen Diphwys, Bonc Moses, Victoria. These levels were served by the 9 pitches of the A series inclines.

The SE side, Braich comprised (successively down from the top): Enid, Assheton Smith, Llangristiolus, Panwys, Egypt, Australia, Pen Garret, Albion, Bonc Roller, Bonc Refail, Sinc Bach Braich, Dyffryn, Bonc Isaf Braich, California, Pen Diphwys, Bonc Moses, New York, Bonc Fawr, Sinc Fawr. These levels were served by the 10 pitches of the C series inclines.

The various other inclines, around the middle of the quarry were designated B.

Gilfach Ddu is at the bottom of the A series inclines the lower 4 pitches of which brought material down from Mills Level to the Padarn Railway loading platforms. These drumhouses have a pair of contracting shoes instead of the usual strap brake and have stops and adjusters that are unique to this quarry, as are the double bar brake rods and finialled cast iron locking pillars. As was often Dinorwig practice, the drumhouse walls and roof extend forward and the backs are fitted with wooden pelmets to improve weather protection. Generally rails are still in situ, with cast check plates at the top and bottom of each pitch. The 2 lower pitches (A1 and A2) have commodious brakesman's cabins with fireplaces and the upper one has also a contiguous office with a "squint" window to view approaching trains of wagons. At this latter point a path is carried over the head of incline by a nice cast iron bridge and a wall bounding the track has heavy slabs cantilevered out to provide shelter for men handling the wagons. Nearby too, is the Anglesey barrack in the form of 20 dwellings, 10 on each side of a street some having the late occupants initials incised near the doorway. There is a sharp turn between A2 and A3 as the later A1 and A2 inclines replaced older ones that ran straight down.

The 5 upper pitches of A are spectacular, but 5, 6 and 7 have been modified to carry cables and the drumhouses demolished.

The topmost (A9) has a very non-standard drumhouse having a lean-to slabbed roof and two separate drums on a common axle, the drum barrelling being sheet iron. The brake, too is curious, consisting of two curved wooden blocks on long timber uprights pivoted at ground level, but the control gear is standard Dinorwig. It is one of the few drumhouses on site (apart from the table inclines) that is of the remote type. Above this there is a small isolated development, not served by any incline but which had a ropeway, the upper sheave, with massive anchor block, being still in position.

Of the C series inclines, the 4 tracked C1 and C2 have gone and C3, 4 and 5, up to Australia level are much degraded. The C6 and C7, table inclines, are unique in that the drums are underfloor in pits below the rails, the brakes being controlled, from cabins, by a sort of ship's wheel, operating a rack through gearing. (This form of brake mechanism is to be seen on some A and B inclines). At C7 the usual cast iron/wooden drum has been replaced by twin sheet-metal drums. C8 has a conventional drumhouse but C9 drumhouse which is a massive stone structure has, curiously, gear almost identical with A9. C10 incline which has massive embanking does not appear to have ever been completed.

There are several other inclines of the discontinuous B series, one notable table incline has a pair of standard drums on a common axle with the two brakes coupled together, the drumhouse is almost totally walled in with, unusually, a jockey pulley for the under-wound rope. Another incline is four-tracked with a double width drumhouse having 2 co-axial, handed drums. Several inclines can be seen as converted to single acting with rubbish filled wagons acting as counterbalances.

On the Garret side, some of the Village level mills are standing as are some compressor houses, weighbridges, loco sheds and other buildings but apart from rail (property chaired on the 'main lines', but bar type, often with slate sleepers elsewhere) and some minor items there are few artifacts. The Garret mills, near the top, have been stripped out.

On the Braich side the Australia mill still has its 36 saw tables virtually intact. They carry Ingersol Rand plates but seem to be of Turner pattern. It is of note that this mill, used right up to closure, had no trimming machines, all trimming being done by hand. Nearby is a compressor house with big Ingersol Rand compressors, one vertical, one horizontal, with D.C. control gear and, behind it, a large cooling water tank. There is also on this level a nice loco shed and a weighbridge complete with all mechanism. In the central area, there is some pit working with tunnels. There is at least one compressor house with horizontal Ingersol Rand equipment. There is a nice cabin, with steel blast shutters containing a winch for a rope incline and partly demolished, an all metal rope incline drumhouse. Lower down is the big pit, tunnels etc. of Matilda. There are now no traces of Wellington mill, which was near the lakeside. (29)

DIPHWYS
Old name for later Victoria district of Dinorwig.

DONNEN LAS SH553597
Tiny surface working.
Remains In forestry. (3)

ELLIS
Old Dinorwig quarry.

FACHWEN Probably Faenol (Vaynol) (SH578615)

FAWNOG One early Glynrhonwy pit.

FFRIDD GLYN Alternative name for Cambrian.

FRONDIRION SH584619
Possible name for early shallow excavation.
Remains Some surface disturbance, considerable amount of fine trimmings. Building remains nearby may have a connection. (24)

FRON HYFRYD SH579617
Tiny early working.
Remains Pit only. (20)

FRONLLWYD
One of the Take Note workings incorporated in Penrhyn in 1785.

GAEN Y GLO Alternative name of Arddu.

GALLT Y LLAN SH601583
Hillside quarry.
Opened about 1811, and operated intermittently over a long period on a restricted scale. Terrace working with central incline.
The ease of working and convenience to the road favoured economic working, but with a high sulphur content the product quality was poor. In 1882 90 tons produced, 3 men employed.
Remains Stone built incline formation and small building ruins. (30)

GARRET
One of the original Dinorwig quarries, giving its name subsequently to a mill and the NW side of the quarry.

GLAN Y LLYN Was part of Glynrhonwy.

GLODDFA FFORDD Part of Glynrhonwy.

GLODDFA GANOL Part of early Glynrhonwy.

GLYN GANOL
Part of Glynrhonwy Upper, for a period worked separately.

GLYN ISAF Part of Glynrhonwy Lower.

GLYN UCHAF Part of Glynrhonwy Lower.

GLYNRHONWY LOWER SH570610
Pit.

Opened in the early 18th C. it was extensively developed in the 1870s. One big and several subsidiary pits, with a large mill and an extensive, locomotive worked, rail system on several levels. (This quarry having been one of the pioneers of internal rail systems.)

Self draining, with all downhill working and the facility of dumping waste into Llyn Padarn made this an efficient unit achieving outputs of 40 tons per man year. The largest undertaking on this side of the valley. Used Hunter saws.

Product was carted to Caernarfon until 1869 when an incline connection was made to a loading point on the main line railway. At one time there seems to have been a connection to the Ffridd incline, but the reason for this is unclear.

The biggest quarry in the immediate area, producing 1789 tons with 70 men in 1883 but later outputs were larger. Closed in 1930s.

Remains Site has been much disturbed by bulk reworking and reuse. (The Air Ministry, which was in occupation from 1940 to 1961 laid down a standard gauge rail network.) There are a number of buildings, mostly modern, dating from wartime factory use. Much of the tramway network can be traced, including the run via a combined tram and drainage tunnel under the road (now blocked) to dump in Llyn Padarn. This tipping area now forms a country park. (13)

GLYNRHONWY UPPER SH565607
Pit.

Mid 19th C. Development, basically two pits in tandem with mills and a most complex partly locomotive worked internal rail network, with spectacularly located tracks including some cantilevered along rock faces. Produced 2181 tons with 90 men in 1882.

Originally connected to Ffridd incline, but after amalgamation everything went out though Glynrhonwy Lower, via a tunnel.

Tonnage around 3000 pa. Closed in 1930s.

Remains Impressive pits with rock-cut tramway formations, some tunnelling, inclines and several buildings. (11)

GOODMAN'S SH572606
Pit.

An early working developed in the 1870s and 80s.

A compact operation with a small mill.

In spite of its small size it had its own tramway connection to Llanberis station, this same line being used for tipping into the lake. Water power believed to have been used for pumping.

Output of a few 100s of tons pa. Closed about 1890.

Remains Very little, some of the tramway traceable. (15)

GREEN'S QUARRY = Goodmans.

GREAVES One time name for part of Glynrhonwy site.

GWAEN Y TŶ Possible alternative name for Arddu.

HAFOD OWEN
Old Dinorwig quarry, near lakeside, site of a big mill. Later known as Wellington. (Near present power station portal.)

HAFODTY = Gallt y Llan.

HARRIET A district of Dinorwig, in the centre of the complex.

HOLLANDS = Chwarel Fawr (552600).

LADAS SH578610
Early hillside working accessed from lake.
Remains Excavation only, alongside Padarn trackbed. (17)

LLOC SH582619
Pit working.
Remains Pit and fine trimming waste, one building. Waste above pit and on other side of road suggests that present road cut through the site. (23)

MARCHLYN SH602628
Hillside quarry.
A late attempt by the Dinorwig company to redevelop on a "Green field" site with a view to winning slate at lower cost, the Dinorwig quarry itself having become expensive to work owing to its dispersion and to indescriminate early rubbish dumping on good slate reserves.
A major investment was made in the 1950s, including an electric mill but at a time of poor prices and shortage of capital, it was not a success. Clooed 1969.
Product removed by motor lorry.
Remains Little on site apart from spoil runs. Buildings were mostly of steel/timber and there was much disturbance during building of the G.E.G.B. Station. (31)

MIDDLE QUARRY = Glyn Ganol.

MILLINGTON
Old quarry, part of Dinorwig.

MORGANS
An old quarry long lost in the middle of Dinorwig.

MURIAU Early Dinorwig working.

PEN CEFN DU Part of Cefn Du.

PEN LLYN SH563622
Hillside quarry.
Very small.
Remains Excavation only. (10)

POTTERS Part of Goodmans.

PREMIER = Glynrhonwy.

SOFIA An early district of Dinorwig.

TURNER Early Dinorwig quarry.

TWLL CHWIL Also Twll Glas and Twll Coch. Old quarries at Glynrhonwy.

TWLL CLAI One pit of Glynrhonwy Lower.

TWLL COCH SH561602
Small pit working, exploiting a red slate occurrence. No mill on site, may have been connected to Ffridd incline.
Remains Scarcely any part from rubbish runs and tramway formations. (8)

TWLL TOMOS LEWIS Part of Goodmans.

TY CLUB Either name of all or upper part of Chwarel Isaf at 579613.

TY DU = Goodmans (or part).

FAENOL (VAYNOL) SH578615
Pit/hillside working, probably very early. Incline was built after 1888, served by Padarn Railway. Disused by 1912.
Remains Tipping run for upper, older working, weigh-house, some small structures and a bridge over road. Access tunnel (blocked) to lower working. On the waste bank a fine run of 7 dressing sheds (in reuse), weigh-house and other buildings, Incline. Pre-incline road down towards lake traceable. (18)

FAENOL (VAYNOL)
Early part of Dinorwig, possibly near Village mills area.

VIVIAN SH586605

Open hillside quarry. Operated on 6 levels, part of Dinorwig, sharing all services but classed as a separate unit.

Remains A spectacular vertical gash in the hillside, with a shallow flooded pit, accessed through a nice archway, with working levels off to the north west.

On these levels, which are connected by steep pathways, some with steps partly constructed of slate sleepers, are a number of fine rakes of dressing sheds and other buildings, some with excellent slab roofs.

The main interest is in the inclines, in 5 tandem pitches, the lower 3 being table inclines with much of the track and gear intact. The drumhouses of the lower inclines are built and ornamented to an almost extravagant standard, the brake mechanisms being unusually interesting, of massive cast construction, operated via spur gears and "ships wheel" controls, with elaborate remote control crimp sprags. The 4-6 incline is most unusual in that there is a continuous run from 6 down to 4 with tracks alongside from 5 down to 4 (giving four tracks on the lower part) both sets controlled from a double drumhouse on level 6. A traverser enabled traffic using the 4-5 tracks to be aligned with the No. 4 drumhouse. On level 2 there is a rubbish run turning out towards the lake near the hospital.

At the foot of the main incline system is a short pitch at right angles to the rest, notable for its underfloor sheave gear and slate sleepers in situ.

Most of the site forms part of a country park and is freely accessible. (25)

WAUN WEN Early digging incorporated into Dinorwig.

WELLINGTON Part of Dinorwig, near lakeside, site of a mill, also known as Hafod Owen.

WEN FAIN One pit of Glynrhonwy Lower.

Nantlle Section 3

General

This area, centred on the village of Talysarn consists almost entirely of pit workings, since the valley floor is virtually solid Cambrian series slate.

With a few exceptions the quarries were small or very small. This was due partly to there being several landowners, and partly due to the perception that the greater the number of quarry leases let, then the greater would be the royalties. Most worked on very confined sites, operating under considerable difficulties as most slate had to be raised, most workings had to be pumped and all had little space for waste dumping, which in most cases had to be put on top of good slate reserves. With the notable exception of Dorothea, few ever made money. Had the land been under one ownership and the whole area exploited as one quarry then a vast and highly profitable undertaking might have emerged.

Technically the area is noted for the ingenuity used to raise material, the considerable use made of Blondins and chain inclines and the vast revetments used to contain waste.

It is a difficult area for the Archaeologist as quarries were worked and reworked, were in close juxtaposition, and were subject to amalgamation, split-ups, renaming and changes of ownership.

Since so many buildings had to be erected on waste runs, many have collapsed. Most quarries have been disturbed by reworking. There has also been a considerable amount of land reclamation that has obliterated all trace of some quarries and destroyed interesting relics in others.

Transport

Originally material was carted to Foryd for loading into small craft for trans-shipment at Caernarfon and later carted direct to Caernarfon.

From 1828 almost all slate was carried by the horse-drawn Nantlle tramway (or, correctly, Nantlle Railway) to the quay at Caernarfon.

This 3′6″ gauge line is important as it was the first public line, laid down to serve the quarry industry. (The Penrhyn railway of 1806 and the Dinorwig line of 1824 were private routes serving only the Penrhyn and Dinorwig quarries respectively.)

In 1867 the L&NWR standard gauge Caernarfon-Afon Wen branch was laid substantially on the same route as far as Penygroes, with a sub-branch to Talysarn in 1872, which then became the terminus of the Nantlle line. However the section from Talysarn to Pen-yr-Orsedd quarry survived until 1963 as the only British Rail horse-drawn line.

All the larger quarries had direct connection, with some smaller ones,

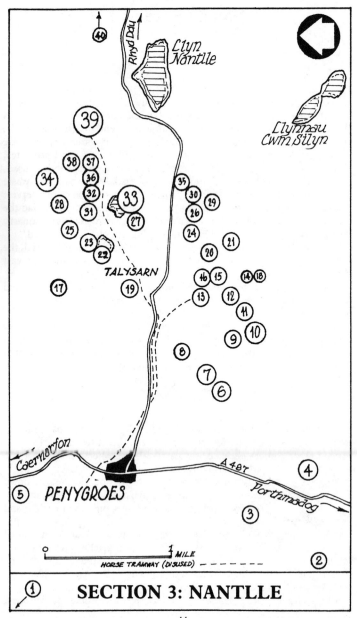

SECTION 3: NANTLLE

on the southern side of the valley, using the short but grandly named Caernarfonshire Tramway which joined the Nantlle Railway about half a mile west of Tal-y-sarn. This line continued as a feeder to the L&NWR line until about 1914.

Those quarries with locomotives used 2' gauge internally, with 3'6" for finished product dispatch.

The route (or at least the final route, as it was moved several times when quarrying encroached) is readily traceable from Pen-yr-Orsedd to Tal-y-sarn, with a good run of slate sleeper blocks near the Pen-yr-Orsedd end.

The Talysarn-Penygroes section (common to both steam railway and Nantlle), is now a road.

From Penygroes to Caernarfon the standard gauge line is readily traceable, and for the most part occupied the Nantlle trackbed. The notable exception is at Penygroes where the horse line curved through the village streets whereas the steam line ran clear of the village to the south. There is also a fine Nantlle Railway bridge at Bontnewydd (SH480599) and the Coed Helen tunnel (SH482616) which the L&NWR line bypassed and both remain extant. The short route of the Caernarfonshire tramway is partly traceable.

The quay that served first the Nantlle Railway and subsequently the L&NWR harbour branch is now a car park below the castle. The erstwhile offices of the De Winton works on the quay is now the rugby club.

At Foryd (SH452586) the old shipping point may be identified by the slate waste and mooring posts. The buildings probably post-date slate shipment usage.

1.	SH454589	Foryd (shipping point)
2.	458506	Foel Clynog
3.	464513	Gelli Bach
4.	470508	Llwyd Coed
5.	470551	Groeslon (works)
6.	477523	Bryn Castell
7.	479522	Ty'n Llwyn
8.	483525	Twll Melia
9.	484520	Taldrwst West
10.	485517	Tyddyn Agnes
11.	486518	Nant y Fron
12.	486519	Taldrwst Upper
13.	486524	Taldrwst Lower
14.	489517	Fronlog
15.	489522	Dolbebi West
16.	489523	Singrig
17.	489540	Hafod Las
18.	490518	Twll Llwyd

19.	490530	Coed Madoc
20.	491523	Tan-yr-allt
21.	492521	Twll Coed
22.	493532	Clodfa'r Coed
23.	493533	Cefn Coed
24.	494523	Ty'n y Weirglodd
25.	495535	Tal-y-sarn
26.	496524	Ty Mawr West
27.	496531	Cornwall
28.	496537	Allt Llechi
29.	497523	Ty Mawr Green
30.	497524	Nantlle Vale
31.	498535	Blaen y Cae
32.	499535	Gallt y Fedw
33.	500532	Dorothea
34.	500540	Cilgwyn
35.	501526	Gwernor
36.	502535	Old Pen y Bryn
37.	504538	Pen y Bryn
38.	506535	Wern Ifan
39.	510538	Pen yr Orsedd
40.	535532	Talmignedd

ALEXANDRIA = Gallt y Fedw.

ALLT LLECHI SH496537
Pit working, closed 1880s, later part of Tal-y-sarn, subsequently used by Blaen y Cae for tipping.
Remains Tipped-in pit only. (28)

ARTHUR Part of Pen yr Orsedd.

BANGOR & CAERNARFON = Hafod Las.

BLAEN Y CAE SH498535
Small open pit working started about 1830. Material raised by rope haulage to a mill to west of pit, finished product sent down lower part of westerly Cilgwyn incline to Nantlle railway. Some tipping done on far side of that incline. Maximum of about 40 men employed, peak output around 800 tons pa, became part of Tal-y-sarn. Closed 1930s.
Remains Dry pit. Vestiges of mill and some other buildings, tramway formations, remains of a steam Blondin winding engine (and collapsed masts). A fine 4-pitch incline system runs through the site. (31).

BRYN CASTELL SH477523
Tiny trial.
No remains (6)

BUARTH FOTY = Fronlog.

CAE CILGWYN Part of Pen y Bryn.

CEUNANT Y GLAW Early working, at no. 6 Mill, Pen yr Orsedd.
No remains.

CAERNARFON & BANGOR = Tal-y-sarn.

CAERNARFONSHIRE QUARRY = Taldrwst Lower.

CAERNARFONSHIRE SLAB = Tan yr Allt.

CAE YSGUBOR Part of Gallt y Fedwr.

CEFN COED SH493533
A small hillside quarry, the only one, apart from a few on the south of the valley, that did not use pit working.
Material removed by an incline via Tal-y-sarn quarry.
Remains Incline formation. (23)

CHWAREL GOCH Part of Tal-y-sarn.

CHWAREL OWAIN JONES Part of Tan yr Allt, later separated off.

CILGWYN SH500540
Pit working dating from at least the 14th C. By end of 18th C. was a substantial undertaking with, by 1820s, horse-whim haulage.
Idle in the 1840s when there was much illicit working by trespassers, it was restarted in the 1850s and rapidly developed into a large undertaking in 4 pits, with, in 1882, an output of 7430 tons employing 300 men.
There was a steam hauled railway system on the pit floors with tunnels connecting the pits. Steam haulage, including use of wire-rope inclines, Blondins and a steam railway system around the south and east of the pits.
The main mill was to the east with 3 other mills to the south.
Waste disposal space downhill, towards the valley floor was limited so a long rubbish run took waste to the west. Later tipping was to the north, the tipping area being reached by a long horseshoe loop line.
Finished product was shipped at Caernarfon, originally being boated from Foryd, later carted direct. When the Nantlle railway was opened it was reached by an incline through Tal-y-sarn quarry which was also used by Fron (Section 5). In 1881, Fron traffic having been diverted to the N.W.N.G. Rly, and tipping encroaching on the incline a new one was constructed some 200 yards to the east. Finally in 1923 a connection was made via the then disused tipping horseshoe loop line to the N.W.N.G.

Output declined steeply during the early 20th C. Final closure 1956.
Remains Buildings have been entirely demolished and the pits used for council rubbish disposal. The main tramway formations are traceable, some being reused as roadway. The 'Horseshoe' line is still a prominent feature. Both inclines traceable. (34)

CLODDFA BACH Part of Cilgwyn.

CLODDFA'R COED SH493532
A small late 18th C. working that operated intermittently until well into the 20th. Other than in the 1890s tonnages were extremely small, e.g. 1873 8 tons, 4 men! Material uphauled to a mill. Direct connection to Nantlle railway.
Remains Site landscaped. (22)

CLODDFA'R DŴR Part of Cilgwyn.

CLODDFA EDWARD REGIOL Part of Cilgwyn.

CLODDFA EITHEN Part of Cilgwyn.

CLODDFA FAWR Part of Tal-y-sarn.

CLODDFA'R GLANLLYN Part of Cilgwyn.

CLODDFA'R GLYTIAU Easterly part of Cilgwyn.

CLODDFA JOHN MORRIS Part of Cilgwyn.

CLODDFA LIMERICK Part of Cilgwyn.

CLODDFA'R LON Three pits, Hen Dwll, Twll Mawr and Twll Balast, became part of Pen y Bryn 1836.

CLODDFA NANT Part of Cilgwyn.

CLODDFA'R ONNEN FACH Became part of Tal-y-sarn.

CLODDFA'R ONNEN FAWR Became part of Tal-y-sarn.

CLODDFA ROBERT ROBERTS Part of Cilgwyn.

CLODDFA'R TURNER Early name for Dorothea.

COCKLE BANK Part or all of Ty'n y Weirglodd.

COCSYTH BACH Became part of Cilgwyn.

COCSYTH MAWR Became part of Cilgwyn.

COED MADOC SH490530
Pit working opened early 19th C., output in 1883 2879 tons with 135 men employed. Internal loco worked tramway system with 3 De Winton engines.
Cable inclines used. Closed 1908.
Was connected to the Nantlle railway via the Gloddfa'r Coed quarry, but later had its own direct S.G. connection to the L & N.W. Rly. The only quarry so connected.
Remains Site completely landscaped. (19)

CORNWALL SH496531
Pit working opened 1867, but some working on site circa 1760. Possibly by Cornish ex-copper miners. Blondin haulage to a mill on a rubbish bank. Output 1040 tons with 70 men in 1882, increasing towards the end of 19th C. Connected to Nantlle railway. After 1899 tipped to south of the river Llyfni by a timber bridge, (collapsed 1927). In Mid 19th C. became part of Tal-y-sarn. Incorporated into Dorothea 1921.
Remains Large flooded pit, several ruinous structures. (27)

DAVID'S QUARRY Part of Pen y Bryn.

DEWS QUARRY Part of Cloddfa'r Lon.

DOLBEBI = Singrig.

DOLBEBI WEST SH489522
Small open pit, became part of Singrig. (15)

DOROTHEA SH500532
Pit working. Although not opened until 1820 rapidly became the dominant undertaking in the area. By 1848 it was producing over 5000 tons pa with 200 men and by the 1882 its 533 men were producing 16598 tons pa.
It was almost consistently profitable, (until pesistent flooding problems, commencing in 1884 and continuing into the 1920s sapped profits), a most unusual record for a non-landowning slate quarry, ultimately 6 pits, the last being sunk in 1891.
At least 8 waterwheels were eventually used for pumping, haulage and mill power. Steam was introduced in 1841 and by 1864 there were three steam engines on site.
Pioneer users of De Winton locos, although steam traction was not used between 1890 and 1901.

The first of 8 wire inclines, including 2 double and 1 triple, was installed in 1841 to uphaul out of the pit to the (ultimately) 8 mills. These replaced the horse whims and hand-worked turntrees hitherto used and survived until 1957. Unlike usual valley-floor working practice the main mill was at natural ground level rather than on the rubbish so that further powered inclines, some of transporter type, were needed to uphaul waste. Waterwheel worked inclined planes were employed on site.

Steam Blondins, (ultimately 4) placed on the rubbish banks were introduced in 1900, (converted to electric in 1959), and used until 1965 when a road to pit bottom was built.

1906 a large Cornish beam engine was installed to pump the pit which by this time was 550 feet deep, (replaced by electric pumps 1951).

As the quarry expanded the old Tal-y-sarn village was engulfed, some of the buildings being used for quarry purposes and the Nantlle railway had to be re-routed further north. There was an extensive loco powered rail system both at ground level and on top of the waste banks. As with the other large quarries there was 2'g and 3'6"g track on site, some wagons having double flanged wheels loose on the axle to run on either gauge. Final closure 1968.

Remains The site is dominated by the lake formed by the flooded workings, (the depth of water is such that it appears as virtually a single pit). The rubbish banks with fine stone incline formations and magnificent revetments, make this a singularly impressive site. To the south are the ruins of the big integrated mill and many other buildings and remains of hoist gallows and haulage housings.

To the west is the Cornish Engine house which still has the engine complete with boilers. To the north east are some of the old village buildings including the ruins of what was the Commercial Hotel. There are some fine archways and on the old line of the Nantlle railway is a notable double arched retaining buttress. Nearby is a nice flight of cantilevered steps. On top of the rubbish banks are tramway formations and several weighbridges. (33)

DOROTHEA WEST = Vale.

EAST DOLBEBI Part of Singrig.

ELLEN Part of Pen yr Orsedd.

EUREKA = Llwyd Coed, also same name for part of Pen yr Orsedd.

FAEN COCH The south western of the original four pits of Cilgwyn.

FOEL CLYNOG SH458506
Hillside quarry. A mid 19th C. working, originally developed for slate,

subsequently became a flourishing stone quarry.
Remains None from slate working. (2)

FOEL UCHAF = Foel Clynog.

FORYD SH454589
This was the original shipping point for Nantlle slate. Out of use by about 1810.
Remains Some buildings that may be rebuilds of originals, much slate waste underfoot. (1)

FRONLOG SH489517
Small pit working.
Dating from about 1840s. Output 1642 tons, 98 men in 1882. Became part of Nant y Fron. Recently worked on a small scale for its green slates.
Remains Two pits. (14)

FRON HEULOG = Fronlog.

GALLT Y FEDW SH499535
Two small open pit workings, possibly worked on a small scale long before being developed in the 1850s. A steam incline raised material to a 6 saw-table mill. Finished product went out by an incline which crossed and then made a junction with the Nantlle railway. A rubbish run bridged the easterly Cilgwyn incline. Output only a few hundred tons pa with around 12 men employed. Had saw-tables in open air, an unusual but not unique arrangement in the Nantlle area.
One pit ceased in 1870, the other continued until 1930.
Remains A crowded site, several buildings including a small mill. One building, almost intact has the patterned slate roof common in this area. Incline formations, including the powered incline and engine house. Possible launder pillars suggest use of water power. There is a fine privy structure also a shallow stone lined pit about 30 metres diameter of unknown purpose. The big retaining wall is in a poor state. (32)

GELLI BACH SH464513
Tiny pit working, possibly only a trial.
Remains Pit itself. (3)

GLODDFA FACH Part of Cilgwyn.

GLODDFA GLAI Early part of Coed Madoc.

GREEN ARFON = Llwyd Coed.

GROESLON SLATE WORKS SH470551
Established in 1850s, on the Nantlle tramway. Waterpower, launder over main road.
Remains Still in use as Inigo Jones works producing high quality slab, besides usual saws (modern) and planers it has an interesting, possibly unique sand-polisher. Visitors are welcome. (5)

GWAITH NEWYDD Name used both for part of Cilgwyn and of Pen yr Orsedd.

GWERNOR SH501526
Small open pit operated intermittently 1860-1915. Water (turbine?) power mill. Pelton wheel used for pumping and hauling. Rubbish was tipped to the north of the public road. No rail connection, cartage to Tal-y-sarn.
Remains Ruins of small mill and abutments of rubbish run bridge. (35)

HAFOD LAS SH489540
Small but early pit working possibly 17th C.
Originally pit was pumped by a waterwheel but in 1807 a steam pump was installed, the first in the industry. It collapsed into the pit in 1817. Direct incline connection to Nantlle railway. Closed by 1880.
Remains Almost nothing, some tramway formations. (17)

HEN DWLL This name used for part of Cloddfa'r Lon, part of Pen y Bryn and part of Pen yr Orsedd as well as Dorothea.

HEN GILGWYN = Part of Cilgwyn.

HERBERT'S Part of Cae Cilgwyn.

LLWYD COED SH470508
Pit working, small, in 1883 6 men produced 78 tons.
Remains Site cleared, used for tipping. (4)

LLWYD COED BACH = Tyn y Bont Bach.

LLYN Y COED = Taldrwst Lower.

MIDDLE QUARRY Old name for the Twll Mawr of Pen y Bryn.

NANTLLE = Pen yr Orsedd.

NANTLLE VALE SH497524
Open pit/hillside working. A small quarry but one of the larger ones on this south side. Opened around 1860. Water power possibly used for

hauling and pumping, before steam was introduced. A chain incline and also a water balance used. 20 men employed in 1882 but only 150 tons recorded that year. An internal tramway system but no external rail connection, material removed by cart. Closed around 1910.

Remains An interesting site. Several buildings including a nice rake of dressing sheds and an engine house with chimney. There is a stone-lined pumpshaft about 2m square with pump-rods. Haulage incline that may have been waterpowered. Alongside the enginehouse is the firebox and boiler of a semi-portable steam engine. Elsewhere on the site is a wheel pit and nearby a chimney for an engine and winder that were on ground now quarried away. This dated from about 1870s and was replaced in 1890s by the now extant engine house. Near the pit possible Blondin type bases. There is well engineered access road. (30)

NANT Y FRON SH486518
Two open pits, worked from about 1840. Tandem pits served by inclines down to an originally water-powered mill and an integrated mill. Later a third pit was opened below the mill level, it is possible that uphauling was by a double acting water balance. Second wheel possibly used for haulage. Operated intermittently with tonnages, exceptionally, of up to 2000 pa (1682 tons 1882) with a maximum of about 90 men employed. An extensive internal tramway system connected to the Caernarfonshire Slate Quarries Railway. Closed circa 1915 but some very small scale working in the 1970s seeking the rich green coloured product.

Remains A number of buildings including a mill and a manager's house. Stone built inclines, partly in a cutting. The lower incline has a curious tunnel through it for a water course and associated with it a stone covered leat. There are pillars that may be launder supports and blocks that could be wire or chain incline anchorages.

In the mill area is an unusual excavated structure of unknown purpose. (11)

NEW FRON HEULOG Late named for third pit of Fron Heulog.

NEW PEN Y BRYN Northern part of Pen y Bryn.

NOEL = Tyn y Bont Bach.

OLD CILGWYN Part of Cilgwyn, closed by 1873.

OLD PEN Y BRYN SH502535
Small pit working, operated in conjunction with Gallt y Fedw.
Remains Pit and vestiges or rubbish runs. (36)

OWEN'S QUARRY Part of Pen y Bryn.

PEN Y BRYN SH504538

A pit working opened around 1770. In 1882 employed 240 men producing 5083 tons. Eventually consisted of 4 pits with haulages up to a mill area, with locomotive tramway layout. At one time 2 waterwheels used for pumping, later steam used for pumping and winding. A pioneer (1830) user of chain inclines. Blondins utilised until the late 1930s. An incline, with an unusual drum buried under the crimp led down to the Nantlle railway of which it was one time the terminus before being extended to Pen yr Orsedd. The Nantlle line was diverted to the south along its presently traceable route as work at this quarry encroached. After 1836 owned by Dorothea, some tipping was done on Dorothea property. Substantially closed in late 1890s, but some small scale working until the 1940s. The Dorothea company made a late bid to re-open and started to construct a road access.

Remains Much of the eastern part of the site (Hen Dwll) has been covered by Pen yr Orsedd tipping and the Twll Mawr and Twll Balast pits partly filled with water and rubbish. On the older, southerly area, there are ruins of a number of buildings some of which, apart from the 15th C. Pen y Bryn farm, may date from the 18th C. On the newer, northerly mills area are the walls of long mill, a barracks and the chimney of a winding engine house. A tunnel, one of several which gave access to the upper pits is penetrable. Remains of incline formations, drumhouse (with some gear) and several artifacts such as flat rods, vestiges of a bucket pump etc. are to be found. Some tramway formations are traceable with the abutments of the rubbish run bridge onto Dorothea property. The final Nantlle railway route is a clear formation (with stone blocks) and the diversion from the original route can be seen. (37)

PEN Y DITCH Incorporated into Blaen y Cwm.

PEN DWYLLT Early part of Dorothea.

PEN YR ORSEDD SH510538

Open pit working, but was originally developed in 1816 as hillside galleries. Mills built on three successive levels, the first in 1860 and the next, their first integrated mill, in 1870, the upper mill followed in 1898. Output in 1882 was 8251 tons with 230 men but in the next decade was much higher. The first connection to the Nantlle railway by incline via Pen y Bryn. When this area was tipped over direct connection was made to the railway. In final form the pits, which extended down to valley floor level were dewatered by a drain. Blondins and incline used. The 3 mills levels were connected by 2 incline pitches, with a third down to the terminus of the Nantlle railway. There were extensive tramways in 2′ and 3′6″g, locos being used on the former gauge. (De Winton in use until 1960). There was a proposal to form a connection with the N.W.N.G. Rly but it was never built. After closure of the Nantlle line in 1963 road transport was used. As a founder customer of the Cwmdyli Power station it was possibly the first quarry to use off-site generated electric power. In latter days the use of Blondins gradually ceased, a lorry road being built down into the one pit in use in the early 1980s. Immediately prior to closure in 1984 12 men were employed with only the top mill being used. Small scale working from late 1980s.

Remains There are the 4 pits (named William, Ellen, New and Eureka), but being partly rubble filled do not now reach their full depth. There are 4 access tunnels and a drainage tunnel.

On the upper level are the structures and machine cabins (some with electric winches intact), of six, locally made, Blondins, some with quite complex pulley arrangements, (due to the fact that towers had to be moved while winding houses were fixed). There are various buildings including the mill with an Anderson Saw table, 10 Greaves dressers and a belt conveyor for mill waste. There are numerous artifacts on site including wagons and much trackage.

On middle level there are various office and other buildings, a ruined mill and one mill virtually intact. This latter, laid out on an unusual back-to-back manner contains unique examples of De Winton saw tables with hydraulic table drive. A separate building, with an adapted shaping machine is laid out as a 'specials' department. There is a workshop with lathes etc.

On the lower level are further buildings including a mill with shafting and other machine remains. Some buildings have signs of late renovation.

The drumhouses and inclines are in unusually fine condition with track on the ground and hinged wooden crimp sprags. There are pleasing 'sentrybox' type banksman's shelters. Gear is conventional except for the use of pulley and weight counterbalances for the brake levers.

At the Nantlle railway terminus at the foot of the lowest incline are stables etc. associated with the line, including a building with a wheelpit alongside, where horse feed was prepared.

The well-known war memorial that was on site has been removed for safekeeping. (39)

PLAS DDU Part of Tan yr Allt, later independant.

PWLL FANOG SH494533?
Small 18th C. working, now vanished under waste.

SOUTH DOROTHEA Alternative name for Cornwall.

SINGRIG SH489523
Small open pit working, possibly never mechanised. Tipping area extended across public road by a bridge. Not rail connected although at turn of century this was proposed.
Remains Dressing sheds, abutments of road bridge. (16)

TALDRWST LOWER SH486524
Open pits. Very small possibly worked up to 1930s. May have been connected to Caernarfonshire S Q R. Stated to have had 2 waterwheels. *Remains* Virtually nil. (13)

TALDRWST UPPER SH486519
Open pits, very small.
Remains Ground disturbance only. (12)

TALDRWST WEST SH484520
Small pits.
Remains Virtually none. (9)

TALMIGNEDD SH535532
Hillside quarry.
Remains Forestry and other work has obliterated all but some traces of inclines. (40)

TAL-Y-SARN SH495535
Pit working, opened in 1790 and became 3rd or 4th largest in the valley with a tonnage of 8210 in 1882 with 400 men employed. (This includes Ty Mawr.) By 1829 a water balance in use. Rag and Chain pumps used. Used steam for hauling by rope inclines. Had locos in internal rail system, but reverted to horse working before end of 19th C. Blondins used. Connected to Nantlle railway by incline. As it developed Nantlle rly was resited further south. Closed finally 1946.
Remains Flooded pit. Some ruinous buildings, remains of incline, several artifacts including a self-contained steam winch in excellent condition. (25)

TALSARN BACH Part of Tal-y-sarn.

TAL-Y-SARN WEST Old name Ty Mawr West.

TAN-YR-ALLT SH491523
Open pit, opened in 1805 material uphauled to north and a mill later built on waste on far side of public road. Worked intermittently, tonnage of 1000 with 40 men employed, recorded in 1873 was possibly exceptional peak. Some very small scale working up to 1980s. Was connected to Caernarfonshire S Q R via Fron Heulog. Stated to have had up to three waterwheels (one for pumping?)
Remains Flooded pit. Some sheds from late working, uphaulage incline formation and vestiges of early buildings, including possible barracks, wheelpit and abutments of bridge across road. (20)

TWLL ARTHUR Part of Pen yr Orsedd.

TWLL BACH Part of Dorothea.

TWLL BALAST Part of Cloddfa'r Lon, later Pen y Bryn.

TWLL CALED Part of Pen yr Orsedd.

TWLL COCH Part of Dorothea.

TWLL CHEINIA Part of Cilgwyn.

TWLL Y CHWIL (Glas a Coch) Part of Cilgwyn.

TWLL COED SH492521
Small hillside working producing green slate, was for a time, part of Tan-yr-allt. Operating in 1970s.
Remains Some modernised buildings, with H. Owen & Sons saw table, Williams Porthmadoc (Greaves type) dresser. (21)

TWLL Y FFACTRI Part of Tal-y-sarn.

TWLL FIRE Small pit working became part of Dorothea.

TWLL GALLT Y FEDW = Cae Ysgubor.

TWLL GOCH 1840s development, became part of Dorothea.

TWLL ISMALIOD North-westerly part of Pen y Bryn.

TWLL JOHN FFOWC Was part of Ty Mawr East, worked independently in 1890s.
Remains None identifiable.

TWLL LLWYD SH490518
Small hillside working, was part of Tan-yr-allt, operating on a small scale in 1980s, using virtually pre-19th C. methods of crowbarring rock.
Remains Small modern building with locally made diamond sawing machine. Interesting "homemade" sawing machine on old lathebed. Warehouse type weighing machines. (18)

TWLL MAWR Part of Pen y Bryn. Name also used for parts of Pen yr Orsedd and Tal-y-sarn.

TWLL MELIA SH483525
Small pit, part of Taldrwst.
Remains Almost nothing. (8)

TWLL MÛG Part of Gallt y Fedw.

TWLL PENBRYN Part of Cae Cilgwyn.

TWLL PENDITCH Part of Tal-y-sarn.

TWLL PENPARC Part of Tal-y-sarn.

TWLL SHAFTYDD Part of Pen yr Orsedd.

TWLL SHED Part of Pen yr Orsedd.

TWLL TÂN Part of Dorothea.

TWLL TYDDYN = Gloddfa Glai.

TWLL UCHA Part of Dorothea.

TWLL Y WEIRGLODD Part of Dorothea.

TYDDYN AGNES SH485517
Small pit working, active in 1860s/70s possibly used water power.
Directly connected to C S Q R which passed through the site.
Remains Some buildings including a possible mill, a dam and railway
formations, tip part filled with refuse. (10)

TY MAWR EAST = Nantlle Vale.

TY MAWR GREEN SH497523
Small pit working, formerly part of Nantlle Vale.
Remains Some small buildings. (29)

TY MAWR WEST SH496524
Pit and hillside quarry developed into open pit. Access to pit by an open
cut. Later, as work progressed downwards, by Blondin. Active in 1860s
with up to 40 men employed but tonnages well under 1000 pa. Material
reduced in a small mill and taken to the road by a long, shallow incline.
Closed 1930s.
Remains Pit, adit and shaft. A number of buildings, mill, Blondin bases
and concrete machinery base possibly for late oil engine. Remnants of an
interesting "lash up" balanced wire incline used in late re-working of tips.
The fine, embanked incline is now much eroded. (26)

TY'N LLWYN SH479522
Extremely small pit working.
Remains Pits and vestiges of buildings. (7)

TY'N Y WEIRGLODD SH494523

Possibly early 19th C. pit/hillside working producing green and red slate. Mill to north west of pit. Haulage incline, may have been water powered. Gas engine, and later, oil engine used. Steam Blondin used. There was incline to road. Closed 1953.
Remains Site used for bulk fill, some vestiges of buildings and a house that clearly predates the quarry. Some concrete bases. Wheelpits and vestiges of haulage incline much collapsed. The apparent tramway formation to Fron Heulog is in fact a road built shortly before 1950s closure. (24)

UNITED Once used name Nantlle Vale.

UPPER TYDDYN AGNES Unsuccessful development, became part of Fron Heulog site.

VAIN GOCH Possibly an anglicisation of Faengoch (Cilgwyn).

VALE = Ty'n y Weirglodd.

VICTORIA = Gallt y Fedw.

VRON HEULOG Anglicisation of Fron Heulog.

WELSH GREEN = Ty Mawr West.

WERN IFAN SH506535

Small early working.
Remains Small depression (behind buildings at terminus of Nantlle railway). (38)

WEST DOROTHEA Name at one time applied to Ty'n y Weirglodd.

WILLIAM Part of Pen yr Orsedd.

Y FOEL = Gallt y Fedw.

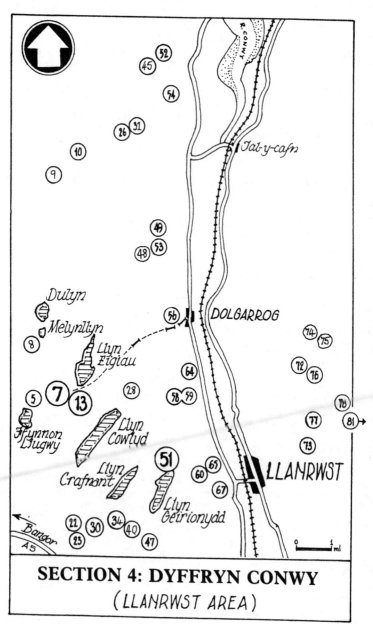

SECTION 4: DYFFRYN CONWY
(LLANRWST AREA)

Dyffryn Conwy Section 4

General

This area comprises Dyffryn Conwy itself and its tributary valleys such as the Lledr and the Llugwy. Slate of varying quality was available at several locations to the west of the lower Conwy, in the Llugwy valley and at the head of Cwm Machno, generally in dispersed locations. There was one area of concentration, in the Lledr valley around Dolwyddelan, winning a poor, intensely black, product. The few sites to the east of the lower Conwy were all tiny, ephemeral affairs.

With few exceptions the numerous quarries were very small and owed their existence to the navigability of the river Conwy, and the presence of reasonable road access to wharves at Trefriw and elsewhere. Virtually all product not used locally went out by river for trans-shipment at Conwy.

The area was regarded as a significant producer during the first decades of the nineteenth century, but the development of transport for better and more abundant slate elsewhere, arrested any great development. The 1870s arrival of the standard gauge line did bring some benefit to a few quarries, but generally it was too late, and still involved cartage journeys.

Although the first Welsh slate to be worked underground was in this area (Clogwyn y Fuwch and Pen y Ffridd), workings were generally open.

Few of the sites have much of great interest, but several of those around Dolwyddelan are notable and both Hafod Las and Rhos have a lot to offer. Also Cwm Eigiau and Cedryn are well worth the long walk.

Transport

Apart from the L&NWR (later B.R.) standard gauge line to Blaenau Ffestiniog (completed 1879), there was no railed transport outside the confines of the quarries themselves apart from a few short lines connecting quarries to a road for cartage.

The most notable of these short links is the fine 2'g, tramroad from Cedryn and Cwm Eigiau to the riverside near Dolgarrog. This 5 mile route ran from the early 1860s to 1888. The Eigiau to Cedryn mill section is just traceable, but from near the Cedryn mill it becomes a road. This road does not strictly follow the tramway route as it is in fact the bed of a temporary steam-worked line for the construction of the Eigiau reservoir, substantially following the old tramway route but making a diversion to avoid a short incline at 745664 near Pwll Du. Some excellent stone embankments are to be seen in this area. The line reached the head of an incline at 765672.

The winding house at the head of the incline, is a later structure, built

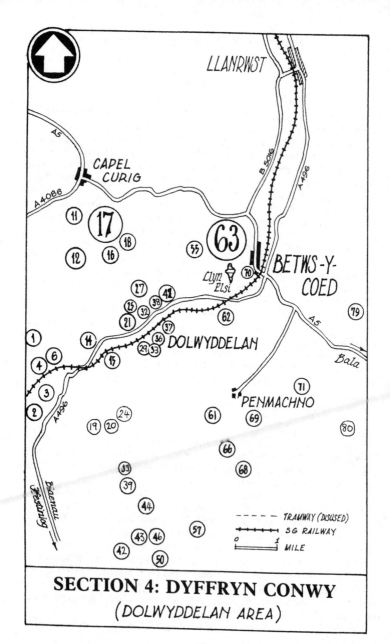

SECTION 4: DYFFRYN CONWY
(DOLWYDDELAN AREA)

on the site of the upper drumhouse of the former 3 pitch incline. This later incline, uphauling for the Cowlyd waterworks maintenance railway, made use of the upper 2 pitches of the slate incline, extended to form one straight run, whereas the lowest pitch of the earlier incline, turned slightly northwards. The bridge under the road of the more modern incline survives but the tunnel which took the earlier line under the road, and the track across the marsh to the riverside has been obliterated.

The incline formation is still in reuse to carry pipes for the works Hydro-electric plant. A feature of the area is the water supply for this plant. Near Cedryn quarry is Llyn Eigiau, now much reduced in size following the 1926 dam collapse. The breached dam and the consequent rock strewn scour can be seen. This reservoir is connected to Llyn Cowlyd by a tunnel from where overground pipes run to the works. The Coedty lake is also part of this scheme and its pipeline joins the main pipe near the head of incline. A further feature is the trackbed of the narrow gauge railway which ran from the head of the incline to facilitate construction of the Cowlyd dam and was retained, until the 1980s for servicing purposes. The engine shed is still in use as a workmen's hut.

There is a network of catchment leats which illustrate, on an enlarged scale the sort of leatwork that was associated with the water supply for many quarries.

There is also a similar, but much shorter tramway, readily traceable, which connected Foel and Rhos quarries, via a 3 pitch incline to a loading point near Capel Curig. It originally tunnelled under the byroad to the mill at the riverside but this section is virtually lost.

Short but with a beautiful embankment and (replaced) bridge is the line that connected the small Chwarel Fedw quarry at Dolwyddelan with the Prince Llewelyn mills.

The only other railed link in the area was the Hafod Las incline down to road level.

Just one quarry, Tyn y Bryn, had direct access to the main line railway.

1.	SH683520	Chwarel Owen Parry
2.	696496	Chwarel Gethin
3.	697497	Moel Drongydd
4.	698512	Hendre
5.	699634	Caerhun
6.	700514	Coed Mawr
7.	701634	Cwm Eigiau
8.	702663	Dulyn
9.	706709	Nant Canolbren
10.	715718 etc.	Bwlch y Ddeufaen
11.	716569	Bryn Engan
12.	717556	Foel
13.	719635	Cedryn

14.	721521	Chwarel Ddu
15.	726519	Pompren
16.	727569	Cae Gwegi
17.	729564	Rhos
18.	729567	Adwywen
19.	730492	Chwarel David Hughes
20.	732492	Cwm Penamnen
21.	735526	Chwarel Sion Jones
22.	736604	Coed y Fron
23.	737597	Clogwyn Mawr
24.	738495	Creigiau Geuallt
25.	738529	Adwy'r Dŵr
26.	738733	Tal y Fan
27.	740539	Ffridd Bryn Moel
28.	741643	Siglen
29.	742521	Tyn y Bryn
30.	742601	Manod
31.	743733	Ffriddlys
32.	744528	Prince Llywelyn
33.	746522	Penllyn
34.	746602	Cornel
35.	748472	Glyn Aber (tunnel)
36.	748525	Chwarel Fedwr
37.	748528	Buarthau
38.	749537	Rhiwgoch
39.	750471	Cwm Machno
40.	751601	Cynllyd
41.	752539	Ty'n Afallen
42.	756452	Foel Rudd
43.	756464	Moel Marchyria
44.	756466	Rhiwfachno
45.	756757	Llechan Uchaf
46.	757464	Blaen Nant
47.	757597	Tal y Llyn
48.	757683	Rowlyn
49.	757693	Pen y Gaer
50.	758452	Tan y Rhiw
51.	759618	Clogwyn y Fuwch
52.	759762	Waen y Fedwen
53.	760688	Penlan
54.	760745	Trecastell
55.	767558	Bwlch Gwyn
56.	767672	Porthllwyd
57.	769464	Hafod Gwyrd
58.	773642	Ardda
59.	775642	Cae Rhobin

60.	776612	Pen y Ffridd
61.	779499	Moel Pen y Bryn
62.	779533	Chwarel Glyn Lledr
63.	779562	Hafod Las
64.	779651	Cae Coch
65.	782618	Pant y Carw
66.	783482	Pen y Bedw
67.	788610	Gwydir
68.	788476	Llechwedd Oernant
69.	792498	Hafodwryd
70.	797552	Beaver Pool
71.	819509	Hwlfa
72.	825654	Cae Madoc
73.	827627	Henblas
74.	827666	Pennant Ucha
75.	829663	Gwern Bwys
76.	831651	Ffridd Uchaf
77.	834637	Cefn Coch
78.	844642	Liberty
79.	849545	Brynhaul
80.	862492	Rhyd Goch
81.	881635	Tyddyn

ADWY'R DŴR SH738529
Small underground working, possibly part of Prince Llywelyn.
Remains Collapsed working, flooded access tunnel. (25)

ADWYWEN SH729567
Possible trial.
Remains Excavation only. (18)

ARDDA SH773642
A tiny hillside working possibly first quarter of 18th C.
Remains Pit and access track. (58)

BEAVER POOL SH797552
A small hillside working possibly active around 1850s.
Remains Possible vestiges in forestry. (70)

BLAEN NANT SH757464
Small hillside working.
Remains Almost nothing, possible excavation. (46)

BRANDRETH = Rhiwgoch.

BRYN CYPLE = Foel.

BRYN ENGAN SH716569
Putative site.
Remains Lost in forestry. (11)

BRYNHAUL SH849545 Putative site.
Remains No evidence of slate working. (79)

BUARTHAU SH748528
Possible trial site.
Remains In forestry. (37)

BWLCH = Prince Llywelyn.

BWLCH CYNNUD = Prince Llywelyn.

BWLCH Y BEUDY = Chwarel Ddu.

BWLCH Y DDEUFAEN SH725718, 722720, 715718
Tiny underground workings without surface shelter of any kind,
probably worked on an "as required" basis.
Remains Excavation only. (10)

BWLCH GWYN SH767558
Open quarry of moderate size operating late 19th/early 20th C. Material
trammed some 150 yards to a mill that may have been water powered.
Product almost entirely slab which was carted by road to Betws-y-coed.
Remains Site is now in forestry but some buildings are discernable
including the old Bwlch Gwyn farmhouse that was reused for the quarry
operation. Outside of the afforested area are the abandoned dwellings of
the quarry village of Rhiwddolion which included terraces and a chapel.
This community outlasted the first world war closure of the quarry, the
quarrymen finding alternative employment mainly in Blaenau Ffestiniog.
There is a delightful slate flagged path leading from the village to the
chapel and quarry.
Much of the access road is traceable. (55)

BWLCH Y LLAN FRAITH = Ty'n y Bryn.

CAE COCH SH779651
Putative site possibly not slate.
Remains Excavation only. (64)

CAE GWEGI SH727569
Underground trial.
Remains Adit, some spoil. (16)

CAERHUN SH699634
Trial? May have not been separate from Cwm Eigiau.
Remains Excavation only. (5)

CAE RHOBIN SH775642
A small and primitive open quarry on a difficult site, with workings tramming to a mills area. Intermittently worked over many years with final closure in the 1920s. Present public road provided access.
Remains Two buildings, one sunken with steps access and a stocking area in front, the other with engine holding down bolts possibly contained a saw. Much waste and trimmings, some tramway formations. Two small pillars of unknown purpose. Possibility of water power but no physical evidence of this. (59)

CAE FFYNNON Possibly Cae Madoc.

CAE MADOC SH825654
Shallow pit working. Surprisingly, in 1867 a sale offered a 10 hp steam engine, 2 saws and 2 planers.
Remains Rubbish runs, tramway, mill building in reuse. (72)

CAPEL CURIG = Rhos.

CEDRYN SH719635
A small and remote quarry with hillside and possibly underground workings, connected by incline and bridge to a water powered mill on the opposite side of the valley. Horizontal and/or Hunter saws used. Opened early in the 19th C. Originally material was carted to Tal-y-cafn but in the 1860s a remarkable 5 mile tramway, reaching a shipping point at Dolgarrog by a fine balanced, 3 pitch, incline, was constructed. Closed about 1880.
Remains Little on the site itself. A well engineered cart road rises past a rake of barracks to the original working. The incline has a collapsed drumhouse part way down, where it was truncated to suit later, lower working. A third working is reached by a tunnel.
The embankment that connected to the mill across the valley is obvious but the wooden bridge over the river has gone.
The mill, which had Hunter and other saws, is ruinous, there is a wheelpit alongside and mountings, apparently subsequently raised up, for the drive shaft. There is an unusual rubbish trackway. Alongside the mill there is a small reservoir and some leatwork. The tramroad can be readily traced. (13)

CEFN COCH SH834637
Possibly not slate.
Remains Pit at roadside. (77)

CEFN MADOC = for Cae Madoc.

CHWAREL DAVID HUGHES SH730492
Small open working.
Remains Excavation only. (19)

CHWAREL DDU SH721521
A small open working developed into a pit on three floors with trial underground. Late 18th C. sporadic working until 1860s output a few hundred tons p.a. (revival attempt 1920s). Material uphauled and rubbish tipped on the far side of the road via a bridge. No mill. Cartage to Trefriw.
Remains Pit, some small buildings, including winding/pumping house (steam?, 1920s oil?) and incline formation. When the road was built (circa 1845) it cut through the rubbish run, which was then bridged. Much disturbed late 1980s by new road works, when relics of iron sheathing for wooden rails also a 'Dog-bone' sleeper of Thomas Hughes rail, were found. (14)

CHWAREL ANDREAS = Chwarel Gethin.

CHWAREL FEDWR SH748525
An open working of early date. Material was brought down a short incline and across the river Lledr by a causeway and bridge, latterly into the Prince Llywelyn mill. Cartage to Trefriw. Closed around 1890s.
Remains Site and incline now almost lost in forestry. The incline is cut by forestry road and the rail underpass is blocked. There are drumhouse walls and vestiges of several dressing shed. The causeway and (rebuilt) bridge are a prominent and pleasing feature. (36)

CHWAREL GETHIN SH696496
A tiny unmechanised underground working around the 1870s, and named after Gethin Jones the well-known local contractor and builder of the Lledr railway viaduct. Originally material from the adits was lowered by a short incline for carting down valley, but later work at new, lower adit tipped over this incline. At one time a big future was predicted.
Remains Incline and a small building, one adit penetrable to a small chamber. (2)

CHWAREL GLYN LLEDR SH779533
Possible site.
Remains Lost in forestry. (62)

CHWAREL OWEN PARRY SH683520 (etc.)
Three separate trial adits, the middle one seems to have possibly yielded product.
Remains Traces of a small building. (1)

CHWAREL IFAN LLOYD = Chwarel Gethin.

CHWAREL RHIWDDOLION = Bwlch Gwyn.

CHWAREL SION JONES SH735526
Small open pit.
Remains Possibly the modernised house may have been connected. (21)

CLOGWYN MANOD = Manod.

CLOGWYN MAWR SH737597
Tiny isolated working. Trial only?
Remains Excavation only. (23)

CLOGWYN Y FUWCH SH759618
Mostly underground, possibly 18th C. Operated by Turner when he came from the north of England in 1812 before moving on to Blaenau Ffestiniog and could hence be the prototype for underground operations in Wales. The series of large openings up the hillside and the use of a cut-and-cover entrance are redolent of Lakeland practice. An unusual site with workings on 6 levels going into a near vertical scarp some 400' on very steeply sloping ground. Originally sledges used, but later an incline brought material down to road level. In spite of producing a small irony and perishable slate, work continued into the 20th C. Much was used locally but Trefriw could have served as shipping point. Output around 200/300 t.p.a. Unmechanised.
Remains There has been some disturbance at the foot of the site, but there is the ruin of a small building, a working area and a chamber going straight in from the hill-face. Access through waste tipped from above by a cut-and-cover tunnel. Level 2 is a tiny working, clearly non-productive. Level 3, a considerable distance above has a twisting strike tunnel leading to some pillared chambering that just breaks into level 4. Outside there are several dressing sheds, those beyond the incline reached by a bridge. Level 4 is chambered in for some 300', at the far end there are footboards still in situ for a roofing tunnel development. There is small forge underground. On the surface there are several buildings including a small smithy and the remains of the remote type drumhouse at the head of the main incline.
Level 5 has, underground, largely been chambered out from level 4. On the surface buildings include a curious circular construction with a rock "bench" around the inside. There are possible traces of an incline down to level 4. Level 6 some traces of small buildings, underground it has been chambered through from below. All structures are primitive and in poor condition. (51)

COED MAWR SH700514

A small open pit, with a short, intermittent life from about 1870. Haulage up, and pumping possibly by waterwheel (source of water uncertain, but said to be by inverted siphon from Ceunant Tynddol), later by steam engine set on the rubbish bank, very much in the Nantlle manner. Unlikely to have had any mill. Transport by cart down valley.

Remains Several buildings including engine house and a forge. Curious small square aperture penetrates the retaining wall alongside the incline formation, possibly for the pump pipe. (6)

COED Y FRON SH736604

Putative site.

Remains Not positively identified, possibly lost in forestry. (22)

CONWAY VALE = Cae Rhobin.

CORNEL SH746602

A small hillside quarry worked successively downwards. Reduction in a small mill, which was, latterly at least, oil engine driven. Closed 1920. Transport by cart down valley.

Remains Two buildings in use as dwellings, vestiges of a possible incline. No evidence of water power having been used. (34)

CRAIG CELYNIN = Ffriddlys.

CREIGIAU GEUALLT SH738495

Putative site.

Remains Possible scratching, not identifiable as slate. (24)

CRIMEA = Chwarel Gethin.

CWM EIGIAU SH701634

A small open quarry connected by an 1863 extension of the Cedryn tramway. Opened prior to 1840 closed by end of 1900s. In spite of elaborate (and expensive) development, production cannot have reached 1000 tons pa.

Remains A most interesting site. Open workings on 5 terraces with an incline to a mill. Possible evidence of a previous incline and of direct tramming from a low level subsequent to use of incline. A curious short incline may have been a temporary uphaulage incline balanced by rubbish. There is some unfinished work above drumhouse level.

An extensive mill is very ruinous but it is clear that the shafting from the central wheel was external. Horizontal and/or Hunter saws believed to have been used. There is a massive leat embankment and some small supply reservoirs and leatwork. There is a barracks, workshop, powder house and several other buildings, and traces of buildings. During successive operating periods, undoubtedly redundant structures were robbed to build new ones, making it difficult to interpret the site. For instance, it is possible that there are the ruins of up to four separate mills. A cast iron "kinked" sleeper and a possible Thomas Hughes rail, have been found.

Beside the tramway formation to Cedryn, the earlier cart road is traceable. A curious relic on site is what appears to be a "rock cannon". (7)

CWM FYNNADOG = Hendre.

CWM MACHNO SH750471

A substantial undertaking working as an open quarry on several levels as well as underground. Connected by balanced inclines to a water powered mills area at village level. Locos were used. Employed 70 men in 1872. It suffered from lack of rubbish tipping space and transport difficulties. There were proposals to connect to the Rhiwbach quarry by a tramway either on the surface or even via the latter's drainage tunnel, but throughout its life road access only was available involving a long cartage to Trefriw, or later, to Betws-y-coed. Finally closed 1962.

Remains A number of inclines in a confusing pattern with newer work overlying older construction reflecting the constricted nature of the site. There are a number of buildings mostly very ruinous but several of the mills are and some of the drumhouses are in a good state. There are some fine rubbish retaining revetments but the impressive castelated wall alongside the road and other features were landscaped in the 1980s. The adits to the underground workings are lost. Above the site is a reservoir. (39)

CWM PENAMNEN SH732492
Putative open quarry.
Remains Possible excavation. (20)

CYNLLYD SH751601
Putative site.
Remains Not identified. (40)

DOLGARROG = Porth Llwyd.

DOLWYDDELAN = Chwarel Ddu.

DULYN SH702663
Possible trials.
Remains Excavations. (8)

EAST ARVON = Bwlch Gwyn.

FOEL SH717556

Open quarry, developed into pit. Opened circa 1835, it operated on five levels with tunnel access to the pit on two. There were two mills on site, the upper one being powered by a waterwheel, possibly with sandsaw and a lower one, which may have supplanted it, having a turbine or Pelton wheel driving circular(?) saws. There was for a short time in the 1860s a mill at Pont Cyfyng (735570) which had sandsaws, possibly later replaced by circular saws.

Material went out by an incline to a tramway which led via further inclines to the road, at one time passing under the road to the Pont Cyfyng mill. Later this was truncated and turned to serve a loading point at 734572 from where product would have been carted to Trefriw. Closed in 1880s but continued to trade, renting their inclines to the Rhos company.

Remains At the lowest level there is a small mill building with vestiges of the turbine supply and some other structures including a possible barrack also a tunnel to the pit. Above, connected by an incline, there is another working level with ruins of a small mill with a wall screening the wheel site, which, unusually, is traversely placed, with launder pillars leading to it. There are some other structures including a forge. There are a number of dressing sheds the most notable being a rake of three with cantilevered slab roofs. There is a second tunnel which like the one below has been blocked, to keep the pit flooded up as a water supply for Rhos. At this level is a possible horse-whim circle and a substantial rubbish-run that has been resited to enable the workings to progress. There are several much degraded internal inclines, and a further possible barracks.

There is some interesting leatwork on the hillside above and a small reservoir, seemingly inadequate to supply either of the on-site mills.

The main tramway is traceable past the vestiges of a third barracks, past the Rhos reservoirs to the head of the upper incline with its conventional drumhouse. The lower incline, steeper and shorter than the upper one has a remote type drumhouse and the two pitches are connected by a neatly excavated swan-neck loop. The roadside buildings and dwellings at the foot of the incline are undoubtedly connected with the quarry.

Below the road is the ruin of the Pont Cyfyng mill with a pit for a breast shot wheel. There are massive slate bases for what appear to be reciprocating saws. The old incline down under the road is not traceable. (12)

FOEL UCHA Y FOEL = Moel Marchyria.

FOEL RUDD SH756452

A series of small open diggings.
Remains Shallow pits. (42)

FFRIDD BRYN MOEL SH740539

Putative site, no remains found. (27)

FFRIDD UCHAF SH831651
Tiny open quarry.
Remains Excavation only. (76)

FFRIDD Y BWLCH = Chwarel Gethin?

FFRIDDLYS SH743733
Putative site.
Remains Possible ground disturbance. (31)

GLYN ABER SH748472 (See Section 8)
This is the end of the Rhiwbach drainage tunnel.
Remains The excavation waste and some quarry waste form a now afforested platform. Underground there are rails in situ. (35)

GLYN LLEDR Possibly Hendre.

GORDDINAN = Chwarel Gethin.

GWERN BWYS SH829663
Hillside quarry, shale?
Remains Excavation and rubbish runs. (75)

GWYDIR SH788610
Open quarry, later used for building stone. Just possible it was slate earlier.
Remains Quarry face, much overgrown. (67)

HAFODWRYD SH792498
Small, but did seem to use water power?
Remains Some traces of buildings. (69)

HAFOD GWYRD SH769464
Tiny underground working.
Remains In forestry, rubbish and access track traceable. (57)

HAFOD LAS SH779562
A mid 19th C. open quarry that was extensively, and expensively developed in the last quarter of the century, in 1883 11 men employed producing 289 tons, but typical tonnages were greater, but cannot much have exceeded 1000 tpa.
Worked on 4 levels and, unusually, the upper levels do not seem to have been entirely abandoned as work progressed downwards. The main mill was on the third level down, blocks from the lowest level being raised by a most unusual power conversion of the main incline. This main incline lowered finished product to a loading point from where it was carted to

Trefriw, or latterly to Betws-y-coed. Operated on a very small scale in the 1920s, closing in early 1930s. Much of the product was building block as inspection of houses in Betws-y-coed will confirm (some showing coarse Hunter saw markings).

Remains Even though heavily wooded this is a most interesting site.
The highest level has a hoisting derrick in situ and a tunnel taking a tramroad formation to the head of an incline (with drumhouse) down to mills level.

At the second level down there is an access tunnel, (with a cutting diversion), leading from much collapsed workings, past a weighbridge to the head of another incline. Back from the head of this incline is a neat pit containing underfloor horizontal sheaves with cable ducts leading towards the crimp where there are 2 levers which are controlled by wires, a band brake and a deadlock respectively. As this incline led almost directly into the mill, there is a pile of blocks at its foot to arrest runaways.

At mills level, there is a tunnel into the quarry and a cut-and-cover tunnel through waste, weigh-houses and other ruins and a most elegant mill.
This main mill is in two parts of differing but equally elaborate architectural styles. The earlier, (1862) eastern and has the roof-trusses the 'wrong way round' i.e. on the longer dimension. The later, (1867) western part has attractive doorways upswept to accommodate some kind of gantry. Between the two parts is a large wheelpit reconstructed to house a Pelton wheel and latterly an electric motor.

An underfloor shaft tunnel runs the full length of the two mills and in addition the newer mill has overhead line shaft mounts on its unusual iron gantry structure. Originally had Hunter saws, presumably the overhead shafting dates from their replacement by conventional saw-tables. Sandsaws may have been used on this site.

Close to, but out of alignment with, this newer section is an obviously much older drumhouse. This main incline drumhouse, like the one on the topmost level is larger but less substantial than is usual. Uniquely, it has been converted to power operation from the mill line shaft, with some of the gearing and control rods being still in place.

This conversion enabled this gravity balanced exit incline to double up as a powered uphaulage incline serving the lowest level. A further unusual feature is the remote control for the crimp sprags. In front of the main mill is the ruin of what may have been an earlier mill with a wheelpit alongside. At the back of the main mill the alignment of launder pillars and other ruins suggest a further wheel, possibly an attempt to augment the power of the original wheel.

Beyond the drumhouse is a commodious forge and workshop.
On this level there is an extensive stocking area.
The lowest level has tunnel access to the quarry, a weigh-house with much of the mechanism intact, several buildings including a stable and the incline landing stage.

At the top of the site is a quaint powder house. There are some small dressing sheds from an early date, but clearly product was mainly slab. The nearby manager's house, has a slate lined food store cut into the hillside behind.

Alongside this manager's house is a flat area possibly the site of the 1920s "London" mill, if so all trace has gone. It may have been a wood and sheeting structure that was removed complete.

There are traces of a watercourse from Llyn Elsi which may have supplied a wheel, and the 24″ pipe which is prominent on the ground may have supplied the Pelton wheel or turbine. Near the top of this run of pipe is a penstock with a curious slate gasket.

Surprisingly for such an accessible a site there is much rail and other artifacts to be found. (63)

HAFODYREDWYDD = Hafod

HENBLAS SH827627
Small flag quarry.
Remains Excavation only. (73)

HENDRE SH698512
Small pit working, circa 1840, water power used for haulage and pumping, possibly steam may have been used later. At some time a horse-whim used for uphauling rubbish. In 1882 6 men produced 120 tons, but earlier tonnages higher. Closed early 1900s. Transport by cart down valley. Characteristic black slate is notable. There was no mill.
Remains Traces of some buildings, two wheelpits, one alongside incline, clearly for haulage, purpose of other unclear. Launder pillars and behind site, site of a shallow reservoir, dammed partly by using natural rock. Traces of horse-whim circle, centre-stone and curved wall. (4)

HWLFA SH819509
A tiny pit, literally a cottage industry, probably worked on an occasional, as required, basis.
Remains Apart from the shallow pit, cottage ruins, with a big, peat style, fireplace and a "workshop" alongside. There is a small turbuary nearby. (71)

LIBERTY SH844642
Very small.
Remains Slight traces of excavation. (78)

LLANRHYCHWYN = Pen y Ffridd.

LLECHAN UCHAF SH756757
Possibly very ancient site.
Remains Excavation only. (45)

LLECHWEDD OERNANT SH788476
Tiny pit, possibly only a trial.
Remains Excavation only. (68)

LLEDR VALE = Ty'n y Bryn.

LORD & LADY WILLOUGHBY = Rhiwgoch.

MANOD SH742601
Small partly underground working, possibly with a small mill, disused by 1896.
Remains On the upper level, a working, subsequently worked out from below, some small buildings including a round powder house. On the intermediate level there is a large opening to an excavation which has a small tunnel leading off it and 2 dressing sheds. At the lowest level, a collapsed tunnel and the remains of a possible mill.
There are nice, well engineered tracks to all three levels. (30)

MOEL DRONGYDD SH697497
Tiny scratching.
Remains Almost nil. (3)

MOEL PEN Y BRYN SH779499
Trial ?
Remains Excavation only. (61)

MOEL MARCHYRIA SH756464
Very small open quarry.
Remains Almost none. (43)

MOEL SIABOD = Foel.

MYNYDD DELWYN = Cornel.

NANT CANOLBREN SH706709
Several small pits, trials only?
Remains Traces of digging. (9)

PENLAN SH760688
Underground. Although a company was floated around 1860 to exploit this site it is unlikely that much, if any, saleable product came out.
Remains Adit (blind) accessed by a bridge, possible second trial adit, some building remains, spoil. (53)

PENNANT UCHA SH827666
Hillside quarry, building blocks?
Remains Excavation and rubbish runs. (74)

PENLLYN SH746522
Hillside quarry/pits with adit access opened in 1875 as an extension to Tyn y Bryn, to which it was connected by an incline and tramway.
Remains Excavation, incline and some buildings. (33)

PEN Y BEDW SH783482
Tiny hillside quarry.
Remains Collapsed adit, traces of two small sheds, very steep access track. (66)

PEN Y BRYN = Hafodwryd.

PEN Y CEFN = Ardda.

PEN Y FFRIDD SH776612
Open quarry, part underground, operating late 18th C. to 1865. Finished product carted via Llanrhychwyn, to Trefriw quay.
Remains A very early example of underground working, may have predated Clogwyn y Fuwch. Site now forested, the only structure is a smithy(?) in fair conditions. Stated never to have had any railed transport but set of wheels on axle were found on site. An eerie series of chambers in the original working face, dip down on 5 levels, pillars are so slender as to virtually form one vast cavern. Much fallen rock from old face and from roof.
At the top of the site, at the limit of forestry is a large stone block said to have been used as a pulpit by John Jones, Tal-y-sarn, the Methodist preacher who worked here and also in Cornel quarry in the 1820s. Later he was to become a partner in the Dorothea quarry at Nantlle. (60)

PEN Y GAER SH757693
Possible trials.
Remains Scratchings. (49)

PEN Y GLODDFA = Cefn Coch.

POMPREN SH726519
Pit, a small (100 tpa?) and early (1840?) working. Material hauled out of the pit, possibly by horse-whim, later water power may have been used. Originally hand worked, but later a small water powered mill for a horizontal sandsaw, was built. Product was removed by cart. May have worked up to WW 1.
Remains Pits with adit access. Some vestiges of dressing sheds and a

possible haulage incline. Lower down the site, mill ruins with wheel pit and launder pillars. (15)

PONT BRON BEDW OR Pont y Bron Bedw = Pompren.

PANT Y CARW SH782618
Small.
Remains In forestry. (65)

PORTHLWYD SH767672
Small slab quarry.
Remains Lost in forestry. (56)

PRINCE LLYWELYN SH744528
Open hillside quarry and pit with some later underground working. Believed to be an early user of saws. The original mill had, 4 horizontal sandsaws, later, a second mill brought the total of machines to 9 saw-tables and 3 planers which also dealt with slab from Chwarel Fedw brought across the valley by a tramway on the still extant causeway. Variously, 30′ waterwheel, steam and water-turbine used for power, possibly steam for pumping. Established circa 1820. With an output of 1685 tons (mainly slab) with 74 men in 1882, (may have been more in earlier years), it was the largest in the area. Closed 1917. Product carted out, by road.
Remains Virtually nothing, site has been used for bulk fill and is almost entirely cleared and afforested. Pit is flooded and adits inaccessible. Some traces of inclines. A garage is on the site of the original mill. Cottages possibly associated with the site are in use. There is a reservoir behind the site. (32)

RHIWFACHNO SH756466
Hillside quarry with some late underground development. Opened around 1830 and operated intermittently in conjunction with Cwm Machno, whose mill was latterly used for reduction. Material carted to Trefriw, later to railway at Betws-y-coed.
Remains Two workings, the upper one partly underground, some vestiges of the drumhouses and inclines that connected the two levels and lowered material to be trammed to the Cwm Machno mill. Some buildings including some relatively modern ones, weigh-houses and access tracks. (44)

RHIWGOCH SH749537
Hillside quarry, opened 1860s deepened into a pit, accessed by adits, with some limited underground working. Later the underground Ty'n Afallen workings were brought into common ownership. Production unlikely to have reached 1000 tpa, closed early 1900s. There was a later, and much

larger mill, possibly never completed, built to deal with the expected heavy tonnages from Ty'n Afallen. Both water powered. A water balance raised rock from the lowest level.

Remains Massive pit with some limited chambering off it. A tunnel led to the original mill (now incorporated into a farm building). The large, newer mill lower down the site, only has walls remaining. There is further tunnel access to the pit at this level and also another tunnel, lower down, with traces of an uphaulage incline (water balance?). A tramroad formation leads in from Ty'n Afallen. Near the bottom of the site is a drainage adit, big enough to suggest that material removal was planned. There are several other buildings including a powder magazine. The exit incline (which may never have been finished) crosses a stream by a nice bridge. There is a substantial reservoir above the site. (38)

RHOS SH729564

A large pit working, with extensive use of water power, opened in 1860s. Produced 1285 tons with 45 men in 1882.

At first, material was trammed out of the working via a short tunnel, (later opened out as a cutting), to the nearby mill area.

As work progressed downward a haulage system was powered by the 30' mill wheel. It is likely that this wheel also pumped. There was also an 18' wheel at the mill, which possibly supplemented the larger wheel when the mill was extended to double its original size.

Later a drainage tunnel was cut permitting the use of a water balance and providing a ready route out for waste. This was consolidated into a platform incorporating a wheelpit as the intention was to construct a new mill at a lower level to avoid uphaulage.

Later the water balance was abandoned and a further 18' wheel (that may have come from Nantlle) was inserted into the mill wheel supply to operate a chain incline.

In 1919 a 40' wheel (ex Cyffty lead mine?) was installed working off the mill tailrace to power a compressor.

At some time another tunnel was started from the pit bottom but never completed.

Locomotive power was used in the mill area, a De Winton working from the 1880s to around 1930. Final closure in 1950s.

A tramway connection was made to the Foel inclines, finished product being carted from Pont Cyfyng.

Remains The pit is of impressive size. The headframe of the water balance is in place, (a balance tank is on the opposite side of the quarry), but the incline itself has been quarried away. There are some traces of the later chain incline with its wheel pit inserted onto the main mill wheel supply, with associated sheave mountings etc.

The fine mill, some 300' long, has the wheel behind, at right angles. This wheel has a mounting for some secondary duties, possibly pumping and winding. There are traces of the earlier, smaller wheel.

The mill building has a series of alcoves for use as internal dressing sheds along one side in the usual Caernarfonshire manner, no trimming machines being used. There is an adjacent lavatory using the wheel tailrace.

From the mill tailrace a carefully built stone channel with penstock leads to the big wheelpit for the compressor.

At the lower end of the drainage/rubbish tunnel is the area intended for a new mill with the wheel housing towering up. Although never used it is believed that a wheel was actually installed.

On the commodious mill area is a big stocking ground and several other buildings including a workshop/forge and a weigh-house with its pit converted to a locomotive inspection pit. There is some underground leating for water pumped out of the pit. Nearby is a rake of barracks/dwellings, part of which latterly housed a diesel generator.

Immediately behind the uppermost wheel is a small holding pond and behind that the lower reservoir which has a three-ply dam reinforced by bridge rail and slate slab. The upper reservoir still holds water. The access tunnels of Foel quarry have been stopped up to provide further water storage.

The tramway and inclines are readily traceable. (17)

RHOS Y GOELCERTH = Rhos.

RHYD GOCH SH862492
Putative site unlikely to be slate.
Remains Obvious quarry face. (80)

ROWLYN SH757683 (?)
Putative site associated with British Slate Company proposals in 1860, almost certainly never produced.
Remains Possible excavations. (48)

SIGLEN SH741643
Possible trial.
Remains Excavation only. (28)

TAL Y FAN SH738733
A tiny, primitive quarry, possibly 16th C., two small faces worked.
Remains Two dressing sheds, another tiny building and a powder house. There is evidence of power drilled holes, but this was from fairly late, small-scale exploitation. In spite of its comparative insignificance, there is a well engineered road to the site. (26)

TAL Y LLYN SH757597
A small, long abandoned open working, going into overhang. Final access by a cutting.

Remains Large trees growing out of rubbish runs, vestiges of one or possibly two dressing sheds, access track traceable. (47)

TAN Y RHIW SH758452
Tiny open pit worked for a few years from 1828.
Remains Excavation and tip. (50)

TRECASTELL SH760745
Open quarry, possibly not slate.
Remains Excavation only. (54)

TREWYDIR = Foel.

TYDDYN SH881635
Small pit working, slab?
Remains Small flooded pit. (81)

TYN Y BRYN SH742521
Begun 1860s, but this may have been a re-start of a much earlier working. Pit on 4 levels connected by inclines to a water powered mill, which from 1875 dealt with Penllyn output.
Sandsaws used, also circular and possibly Hunter saws. Output may have neared 2000 tpa (including Penllyn). Closed 1924. Originally material carted to Trefriw for shipment, but later had a siding from the main line railway. The only quarry in the Conwy area to have direct rail connection. Closed 1930s.
Remains 4 inclines and ruined drumhouses, a number of dressing sheds and other buildings. Remains of weighing machine. Tips have been used for bulkfill leaving little in the mill area other than machine bases and wheelpit. Vestiges of a tramway and incline from Penllyn and to Dolwyddelan station. (29)

TY'N AFALLEN SH752539
Underground working, a small operation started by Joseph Kellow in 1870s, developed, with little apparent success, in connection with Rhiwgoch in the early 1900s.
Remains 2 adits, the lower one has very limited chambering attempts, some rail on ground. The upper with adjacent dressing shed and drumhouse has several small workings breaking out to bank and a steeply inclined shaft downwards. Some rail in tunnel. The incline formation is much degraded. The tramway to Rhiwgoch now partly forms the access road to the farmhouse. (41)

TYN Y DDOL = Coedmawr.

WAEN Y FEDWEN SH759762
Putative site.
Remains Possible excavation. (52)

Y FEDWR = Chwarel Fedwr.

Y FOEL = Prince Llywelyn.

Cwm Gwyrfai Section 5
Area served by N.W.N.G. Rly

General

This area comprises those quarries in the area served by the North Wales Narrow Gauge Railway.

They worked various exposures of Cambrian slate that occurred between Llanberis and Nantlle.

They fall into two groups. Firstly those at the head of Cwm Nantlle which are virtually contiguous with, and worked in ways similar to the Nantlle quarries, but their fortunes (and misfortunes), at least latterly, were so closely allied to the NWNGR that they are included in this section. The depredations of time, of clearance and tipping, limit the remains now extant in this closely packed group of sites.

Secondly those in Cwm Gwyrfai itself. These were a series of open quarries, of varying sizes on either side of the valley, working isolated occurrences. With the exception of Glanrafon and possibly Hafod y Wern all were small. Hafod y Wern and Glanrafon have been much cleared but several other quarries still have interesting remains.

Transport

Until the opening in 1877 (final extension 1881) of the NWNGR provided a rail link, all these sites were handicapped by poor transport. The opening of the line, with its prospect of efficient transport encouraged vigorous development at some of them.

The 2'g 7 mile line ran from Dinas, near Caernarfon, where there were trans-shipment facilities onto the L&NWR Caernarfon-Afon Wen branch, for conveyance either to Caernarfon port or onto the main line network. Thus apart from its technical and financial shortcomings, the double handling at Dinas inflated users costs.

Exclusively loco worked the NWNGR was never a commercial success, it declined during the first years of the new century and was virtually moribund by the time it was incorporated into the Welsh Highland Railway in 1923.

The short-lived WHR development, which provided an extension to Porthmadog, carried little slate traffic as it opened after the industry was well into its almost terminal decline.

The NWNGR may be readily traced throughout its length. Unusually, most of the bridges remain in situ, albeit undecked, most being of a standard, steel pattern. Near Rhostryfan was the Tryfan junction for the Bryngwyn branch. This consisted almost entirely of one impressive

SECTION 5: CWM GWYRFAI

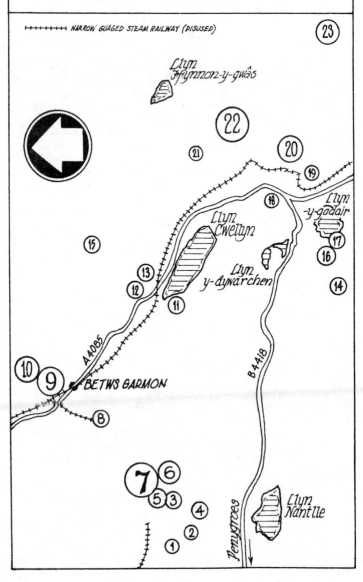

++++++++ NARROW GUAGED STEAM RAILWAY (DISUSED)

23

Llyn
Ffynnon-y-gŵas

22

21

20

19

18

Llyn
Cwellyn

Llyn
-y-gadair

15

17

16

13

Llyn
y-dywarchen

12

14

11

A4085

B4418

10

9 BETWS GARMON

8

7 6

5 3

4

Penygroes

Llyn
Nantlle

2

1

incline. From the head of this incline branches led to various quarries, the one which curved around the north of Moel Tryfan to Alexandra quarry being particularly spectacular. End on to the Bryngwyn incline was the incline from Moel Tryfan quarry and southwards a line (only vaguely traceable) snaked through the village of Fron to Fron quarry. From 1923 Cilgwyn quarry was also connected to this branch via spur of its horseshoe tipping line.

In Cwm Gwyrfai itself the first quarry connection was at Treflan junction near Betws Garmon where a branch swung north over the river to Garreg Fawr quarry and a possible connection with Treflan quarry. This branch also served the nearby ironstone mine.

At Betws Garmon another branch, readily traceable, ran south to Hafod y Wern quarry.

Glanrafon quarry incline was connected by a triangular junction. Rhos Clogwyn quarry was originally incline connected, but later a ropeway was used.

At the Rhyd Ddu terminus a connection was planned to Llyn y Gadair quarry, but was never completed, but this and several other small quarries loaded by cart.

1.	SH510552	Braich
2.	512548	Braich Rhyd
3.	513556	Crown
4.	515548	Fron
5.	515559	Moel Tryfan
6.	519558	Brynferam
7.	519562	Alexandra
8.	530571	Hafod y Wern
9.	538582	Garreg Fawr
10.	539584	Treflan
11.	552552	Castell Cidwm
12.	552562	Plas y Nant
13.	553562	Bryn Manllyn
14.	557500	Bwlch y Ddwy Elor
15.	562565	Lefal Fawr
16.	564518	Gader
17.	564519	Llyn y Gadair
18.	570533	Bryn Cwellyn
19.	573526	Ffridd
20.	576530	Rhos Clogwyn
21.	577547	Bron y Fedw
22.	581540	Glanrafon
23.	600521	Bwlch Cwmllan

ALEXANDRA SH519562

A substantial open pit working with steam powered mills etc. and an extensive loco worked internal tramway system. Opened in the 1860s, at its peak produced 6000 tons pa employing over 200 men. Worked sporadically after W.W.1 and closed in late 1930s, although, after the Moel Tryfan workings broke through it was used as a source by that quarry until the mid 1960s, all reduction taking place in their mill. In its last days all transport was by lorry. Bulk working continued much later. Finished product was taken away by a most spectacular 'Himalayan' line down to the head of the Bryngwyn incline of the NWNGR.

Remains Due to bulk working the site is much disturbed but apart from the pits there are substantial remains of the mills and other structures including possible Blondin bases. The formation of the tramway route is still a most notable feature. (7)

AFON GOCH = Castell Cidwm.

BRAICH SH510552
An open pit working, operated on a small scale from around 1820s with material probably being sent out via Cilgwyn (Nantlle). It was substantially developed in the 1870s when a mill was built, water power for pumping, steam for pumping and haulage via a chain incline, loco working and a connection made to the head of the NWNGR Bryngwyn incline. Output in 1882 2614 tons with 124 men. Closed 1911.

Remains Very little apart from the pit itself and the ruinous mill and other buildings and incline formation. The tramway to drumhead is not easily traced as it crossed boggy ground. (1)

BRAICH MELYN = Braich.

BRAICH RHYD SH512548
A pit working not to be confused with Braich quarry. Older and developed earlier, by the 1870s approached Braich in size. Originally material sent out through Cilgwyn (Nantlle) later material went out on the NWNGR via Braich quarry. Steam was used latterly for pumping and hauling and it is notable that in 1827 windpower was tried for pumping. Closed early 20th C.

Remains Pit, a few ruinous buildings, (including part of the mill, in reuse), vestiges of an incline and internal tramway formations. (2)

BRON Y FEDW SH577547
Trial only.
Remains Small excavation. (21)

BRYN CWELLYN SH570533
Small pit working, one pit accessed by cutting, the other by a tunnel. Tipping on far side of main road. Cart transport possibly to NWNGR.
Remains Little apart from pits. Ground disturbed by road and forestry. (18)

BRYNFFERAM SH519558

Small pit working consisting of two excavations accessed by tunnels. Operated in 1880s and possibly much earlier, output in 1883 252 tons, 18 men. No rail connection.

Remains Nothing other than the pits themselves and some slight traces of buildings. (6)

BRYN MANLLYN SH553562

Very small hillside quarry, if anything was produced, it may have been carted to Plas y Nant, closed before the railway opened.

Remains Working face only. (13)

BWLCH CWMLLAN SH600521

Open pits operated over at least two separate periods. An early working, possibly dating from the 1840s was mechanised by providing tunnel access to a small water powered mill. Later, probably in the mid 1870s, a fresh excavation was made at a higher level with a new mill. A chain incline system may have been used at some time. Two inclines in tandem brought material down. Later a third mill seems to have been built with a further access tunnel to the working. Tonnages were moderate (about 850 tons 1877), mainly slab, and cannot have justified the large volumes of overburden which had to be removed, let alone the investment on site and on the cart road to Rhyd Ddu, via which material was sent out.

Remains On the upper site there are vestiges of a small water powered mill and lower down more substantial remains of another mill, with a prominent launder wall. There are two drumhouses built of country rock. Back from the upper one there is an unusual chamber that may have been for an underfloor sheave mechanism, predating the conventional drumhouse. The lower drumhouse may have had an overhead horizontal sheave.

On the lower site there is the small mill and wheel pit, some tramway formation and a weighbridge. Lower down there is a rake of barracks that would appear to date from the upper or later period of working.

Above the site are the dams of two tandem ponds, of conventional 'three ply' construction. There is also a small holding reservoir for the lowest mill. At the top of the site, where the access track ends, there is some isolated excavation which may have been very early working.

There is evidence of rubbish wagons having been run directly on slate ways, rather than rail, suggesting that in the latter days, at least, this was a marginal enterprise.

There is a nice slate slab bridge on the access road that has been reinforced with 'T' bulb rail and with what may have been round bar rail. There is also some bull head rail nearby. (23)

BWLCH Y DDWY ELOR SH557500

A very small pit working reached by a cutting, unmechanised, output in

1883 160 tons with 7 men. Material was carted, to Caernarfon it being closed before NWNGR was opened.
Remains Almost nothing. Site disturbed by forestry work. (14)

BWLCH Y LLYN Part of Braich.

CAERGWYNION = Bryn Manllyn.

CASTELL CIDWM SH552552
A small hillside/pit working opened mid 1870s, it produced a poor, irony slate. Cart road access along south side of Llyn Cwellyn.
Remains Very little owing to bulk operations at recent date. Vestiges of buildings, access track at original level also a later track alongside the lake. Water available on site but no evidence that water power was used. (11)

CHWAREL GOCH = Castell Cidwm.

CILGWYN Although this quarry was, latterly, a user of the NWNGR, it was for most of its long history very much part of the Nantlle scene. Therefore it has been included in Nantlle, Section 4. The formation of the 1923 connection from the Cilgwyn "Horseshoe" tipping line to the head of the Bryngwyn incline, is clearly traceable.

CLOGWYN COCH = Bryn Cwellyn.

CLOGWYN Y GWIN = Rhos Clogwyn.

CORS Y BRYNIAU = Alexandra.

CROWN SH513556 or New Crown
Open pit with adit to mill.
Remains Traces of mill. (3)

CWELLYN = Bryn Cwellyn.

DONNEN LAS = Bryn Manllyn.

FFRIDD or Ffridd Isaf SH573526
Very small open working, close to Rhyd Ddu station but possibly closed before railway was built.
Remains The distinctive slot like working, quite a lot of spoil for such a small site and two buildings now in reuse. Also an exceptionally fine powder house. (19)

FRON SH515548
Open working, two pits joined by a short tunnel, opened around 1830.

Possibly used water for pumping, but from 1860s used steam for haulage and mill power, a cable incline, replaced a water balance. Peak output may not have exceeded 1500 tons pa, even with 100 men employed, and was less after about 1880 (1883 728 tons with 62 men employed). Some work continued until the 1930s.

Originally material was taken via a tramway to Cilgwyn (Nantlle) but after 1881 the NWNGR was used via the Bryngwyn incline.

Remains Water-filled pit. Some buildings on site, one in reuse and extensive rubbish runs and retaining walls. The tramway through the village to the drumhead is readily followed. (4)

GADER SH564518 or Gader Wyllt or Gader Laich

Open pit, virtually on same site as Llyn y Gadair. 1914 bought by Glanrafon.

Remains Pit and incline, tramway to trial. Partly built mill and other building in reuse. (16)

GARMON VALE = Plas y Nant.

GARREG FAWR SH538582

A small pit working possibly dating from the early 1800s. There was a separate, later, underground development. Operated sporadically until mid 1880s (1883 96 tons, 6 men) and occasionally on a small scale, up to the 1930s. Output originally carted to Caernarfon. There was a spur off the NWNGR iron mine branch, which may have been reached by an incline. If not, then material could have gone out through Treflan.

Remains An interesting site. There is a drumhouse type building (for the incline that was or was not built!) which has been made into a two storey office or dwelling. There is also another 2 storied structure built to resemble a tiny 'castle'.

Apart from the classic type of dressing sheds etc, there is a brick building containing i.c. compressors, a saw sharpening machine and a unique saw-table with 3 speed table drive marked "John Owen Bangor, Menai Iron Works 1875". There are also various ropes, blocks and other pieces of tackle. (9)

GLANRAFON SH581540

Open quarry and by far the largest in the district, only a small scale operation up to the late 1870s, it developed with the coming of the railway, producing 1725 tons with 92 men in 1882 but may have doubled this during the ensuing few years. Consisted of one big and several subsidiary workings. As the main working deepened material was raised by powered incline, or possibly a water balance. Before a drainage tunnel was cut, pumping was done by flat rods from a remote water wheel. Material was originally taken by incline to the large mills area, (double mill with a central wheel), but later a tramway tunnel was cut. There were several locomotives on site. A short, followed by a longer, incline went down to make a triangular junction with the NWNGR. Closed about 1915.

Remains The mills area has been totally cleared, the quarrying area shows little evidence of methodology, and the tunnels have fallen in. Below the site is the pit for the big pumping wheel and some traces of the road supports.

The most notable relics are the 2 storey barrack and a large shed part way down the incline. The fine incline formations make a prominent feature. (22)

HAFOD Y WERN SH530571

A small working developed with the coming of the railway into a substantial undertaking approaching in scale, Glanrafon. Originally a hillside working it deepened into three pits, accessed by tunnels. Material was brought down by incline to mills at valley floor level. Following some years of very small scale working, it closed in the mid 1920s. A branch of the NWNGR ran right to the mill.

Remains The site has been much disturbed by bulk excavation and clearance. Everything in the mills area has gone. There is the much decayed formation of one incline with a ruined drumhouse at its head. The upper part of this incline was abandoned and one can see how it was broken into part way down to serve an intermediate level. No drumhouse was used for this truncated section but a brake leaver suggest that underfloor sheaves were used and may still remain buried.

The railway branch trackbed is still prominent. (8)

LEFAL FAWR SH562565

Putative site of at least trials.

Remains Possible scratching. (15)

LLYN Y GADAIR SH564519

Small open workings dating from about 1885, as a co-operative enterprise and continuing occasional, somewhat unsuccessful, operation until the 1920s. Slate was carted to Rhyd Ddu for loading onto the railway, a causeway for a branch line was built but never railed.

Remains There is a mill building, larger than the site would seem to justify, but this seems to have never been completed. Behind this there is an unfinished tramway to an underground working that was never properly developed.

The most prominent feature is the big "Nantlle style" pit with its uphaulage incline and mill on the rubbish bank.

Two wheel pits and launder embankments suggest waterpowered pumping and perhaps haulage. The incline would seemingly have had to be also used for lowering finished product.

This working originally dumped rubbish in the lake, the run for this being cut by the formation for the uncompleted exit tramway.

At the back of the site is an open working with a small mill and a rubbish run with rail in situ, possibly this was the final phase. There are ruins of several dressing sheds and other buildings (one still roofed). (17)

MOEL TRYFAN SH515559

An extensive pit working. A small site that expanded rapidly in the 1880s following rail connection, employing in 1882, 81 men producing 1880 tons. Locos, (De Wintons) used. Material was taken by tunnel to a substantial mills area, where, unusually for the area, guillotine dressers are believed to have been used.

Finished product went down a long incline to the Bryngwyn drumhead. Latterly when the workings broke through into Alexandra, material from that quarry was reduced in the two Moel Tryfan mills. Working on a small scale until the 1970s.

Remains The site is much disturbed by bulkfill operations and the tunnel has gone. There are extensive, but very ruinous remains on the mills area. The ¼ mile long incline is a nice feature. (5)

NEW BRAICH = Braich.

OLD BRAICH = Braich Rhyd.

PLAS Y NANT SH552562

Small hillside quarry, opened mid 19th C. and closed around 1889, recorded as employing 28 men and producing 672 tons in 1883. An incline led to a small mill. It is possible that there was a tramway connection to the railway.

Remains Very little, apart from some small buildings, including a nice powder house and the incline formation. (12)

PLAS ISAF = Plas y Nant.

PRETORIA Part of Brynfferam.

RHOS CLOGWYN SH576530

An open pit working developed on the 1880s. A tunnel brought material to the substantial mills area. Originally finished product was taken down an incline to be carted away. When connection was made with the railway, this incline became disused and the make was trammed out on the level to a short incline to a siding on the NWNGR. Work ceasing not long after this connection was made. When the quarry was revived on a very small scale in the 1920s, a second, lower tunnel was used, some hand reduction being done in the actual quarry with possibly a portable saw. From this lower tunnel finished slate was taken down to the railway by a short ropeway. Final closure in 1930s.

Remains The 'old', substantially built, incline is a prominent feature. The mills area has been entirely cleared. The two tunnels are open and the tramway and incline to the railway is obvious. At the lower level is the base of the ropeway down the railway and, inside the quarry, a late date dressing shed, with much trimming waste around. (20)

SNOWDON = Rhos Clogwyn.

TREFLAN SH539584
An open pit working, operating in the 1880s and possibly much earlier, and sporadically, later. Probably a maximum of about 30 men employed producing around 7/800 tons pa. Material was brought from two pits by tunnels to a dressing/mills area and finished product went down an incline to a branch of the NWNGR.
Remains The two tunnels lead into the workings. Near the upper one is a fine stone building, probably pre-dating the quarry, which appears to have been used as an office and workshop. Near the lower tunnel is an extensive working area that has been totally cleared except for one small building. At the highest point of the site is a curious structure some 3m x 2m x 4m high, open at the front at ground level and at the back at 'first floor' level. The purpose is unknown. There is water available on site, but there is no evidence that it was used for power. What appears to be a leat is a channel to divert surface water from the workings.
There is the substantial incline down to valley floor level, with a little smithy near where it crosses a road. (10)

TWLL PRETORIA = Bwlch y Llyn.

VICTORIA = Hafod y Wern.

VRON = Fron.

WEST SNOWDON = Bwlch Cwmllan.

Y DREFLAN = Treflan.

Y FOEL Possibly western part of Alexandra.

Pennant/Gest Section 6

Cwm Pennant and coast from Borth y Gest to Cricieth

General

In this area are many very small quarries, producing, or failing to produce, indifferent slate from the tail end of the Gwynedd occurrences. A few are very ancient quarries of convenience, few lasted long and fewer enjoyed any degree of success.

Although most are now just scrapings in the ground there are several sites worth visiting.

Moelfre and Hendre Ddu have notable remains extant and Dolgarth and some others are not without interest.

However both the equally unsuccessful Prince of Wales and Gorseddau quarries have an exceptional amount to offer, particularly the latter, with its unique Ynys y Pandy mill.

With the exception of some tenatative underground at Prince of Wales and trials at Gorsedda and Princess, all workings were open. The tunnelling at Moelfre were only trials.

Transport

Some ancient quarries carted or carried to the nearest point on the coast any product not used in their immediate locality. After the 1830s some may have used Porthmadog.

Prince of Wales and possibly Princess carried over the Bwlch y Ddwy Elor to Caernarfon.

There were plans to connect Hendre Ddu and possibly others on the western side of Cwm Pennant by a rail line to Cricieth.

The one railway actually built was the 8 mile, 3′g Gorseddau Tramway opened in 1857 to connect the Gorseddau quarry with Porthmadog.

It is notable as, apart from the Nantlle Railway which ran over almost level terrain, it was the only quarry-seaport horse-drawn line never to have used inclines.

The line is readily traceable almost throughout its length from the quarry, past the Ynys y Pandy mill to Penmorfa where the road crossing has been lost in roadworks. It is defined by a lane through Penmorfa, drops down in front of the scarp to behind Tremadog, where there was a reversing loop. From there, crossing the main road it used the trackbed of the Tremadog Ironstone tramway, now defined as a footpath, to Porthmadog. In Porthmadog, the line followed the line of present day streets to the port itself.

SECTION 6: PENNANT/GEST

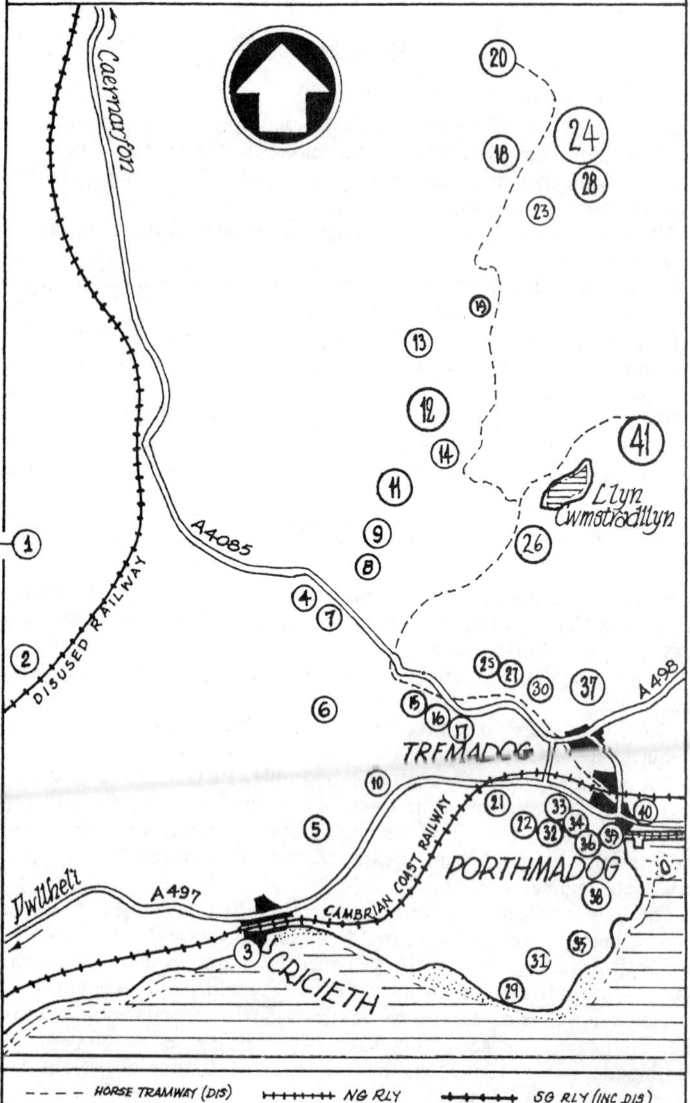

In 1875 the then defunct line was relaid in 2'g and extended from near the Ynys y Pandy mill to Prince of Wales quarry.

It did have one locomotive, but it is doubtful it if had much use. In fact latterly trucks may have been hand pushed.

There was a further, very short-lived extension to serve the mine at the head of the valley. The whole system was out of use by the early 1890s. This extension line to Prince of Wales can be readily traced and it can be seen that though the trackbed is sound the bridges etc. are much inferior to the original works, indeed if the Cwm Dwyfor mine extension is followed (via a delightful cutting) the even poorer standard of construction can be noted.

1.	SH394407	Pont Rhyd Goch
2.	454407	Foel Isaf.
3.	497378	Marine Terrace.
4.	506428	Tyddyn Mawr.
5.	507394	Mynydd Ednyfed.
6.	508407	Ymlych
7.	510427	Ysgubor Gerrig
8.	516437	Dolwgan
9.	518439	Prince Llywelyn
10.	519393	Pencraig.
11.	519444	Hendre Ddu
12.	521451	Moelfre
13.	525461	Chwarel y Plas
14.	532448	Isallt
15.	536397	Bryneglwys
16.	538396	Coed y Chwarel
17.	538397	Garreg Felin
18.	538495	Dolgarth
19.	541469	Cwm Lefrith
20.	541505	Cwm Dwyfor
21.	542396	Cloddfa Shon Prys
22.	544390	Bron y Foel
23.	548483 etc.	Moel Lefn
24.	549498	Prince of Wales
25.	550409	Ty Cerrig
26.	550433	Ynys y Pandy (Mill)
27.	552408	Penmorfa
28.	553495	Princess
29.	554365	Ynysycyngar
30.	554406	Ty'n y Llan
31.	555372	Garreg Wen
32.	559388	Moel y Gest
33.	559393	Penrhynllwyd
34.	561389	Ty Hwnt Bwlch

35.	562372 etc.	Penybanc
36.	562386	Tyddyn Llwyn
37.	564406	Cwm Bach
38.	566382	Garth
39.	567386	Morfa Lodge
40.	572385	Ynystowyn
41.	573453	Gorseddau

ALLTWEN = Penmorfa and/or Ty Cerrig.

BLAEN Y PENNANT = Cwm Dwyfor.

BORTH Y GEST = Penybanc.

BRAICH Y SAINT = Ymwlch.

BRON Y FOEL SH544390
Open quarry dating from late 18th C. Possibly closed by mid 19th C. Material carried in baskets to ship at Ynyscyngar.
Remains Little apart from actual excavation. Present house on site probably associated with quarry. Access tracks. (22)

BRYNEGLWYS SH536397
Putative site.
Remains Possible excavation. (15)

CAMBRIAN RLYS = Garreg Felin.

CHWAREL Y LLAN = Isallt.

CHWAREL Y PLAS SH525461
Small pit working, material carted to road at Plas y Pennant.
Remains Upper working with dressing shed. Lower working, accessed by tunnel, does not seem to have produced. (13)

CAE CRWN = Tynyllon.

CLODDFA = Mynydd Ednyfed.

CLODDFA SHON PRYS SH542396
Tiny scratching circa 1880.
Remains In forestry, obliterated. (21)

COED Y CHWAREL SH538396
Small, early working.
Remains In forestry, obliterated. (16)

CWM BACH SH564406
Hillside quarry, operating in 1920s, possibly a revival of earlier working.
Remains Bases of temporary buildings, zig-zag access track. (37)

CWM DWYFOR SH541505
Almost certainly trial only, dating from 1877.
Remains Adit and rubbish run. All the buildings etc. pertain to the metal mine. (20)

CWM LEFRITH SH541469
Possibly trial only. (1880s?)
Remains Adit and rubbish run. (19)

CWM TRWSCWL = Prince of Wales.

DOLBELMAEN = Tyddyn Mawr.

DOLGARTH SH538495
Hillside working on 3 levels, the upper level almost certainly not productive. Opened in 1870s possibly closed by 1880. Material taken from hillside workings by a balanced incline to a water powered mill on the valley floor. Finished product carted down valley.
Remains Being situated on steep slope, viewed from the opposite hillside it provides a "diagram" of a typical quarry layout. 2 levels, have tramway formations to the head of a steep incline, which has a substantial remote type drumhouse. There are some dressing sheds on each terrace.
Near foot of incline is a massive rectangular structure of unknown use. The mill building is an "add on" to a pre-existing building, another building (dwelling?) is in agricultural reuse.
Notable is the long, slate covered tailrace leat to the river.
Said to have been some copper mining on this site. (18)

DOL IFAN GETHIN = Dolgarth.

DOLWGAN SH516437
Early 18th C. open pit working.
Remains Virtually nothing other than the pits themselves. (8)

FOEL ISAF SH454407?
Putative trial.
Remains Not definitely located. (2)

GARREG FELIN SH538397
Hillside quarry (1830s?) very small.
Remains Excavation, possible building, much overgrown. (17)

GARREG WEN SH555372
Tiny scratching (1880s?)
Remains On caravan site, barely traceable. (31)

GARTH SH566382 & 568383
Small open slab workings.
Remains Possible vestiges. (38)

GORSEDDAU SH573453
A most spectacularly unsuccessful undertaking. A small early 19th C. site, developed in 1855 on a "no expense spared" basis into a terraced hillside quarry on 9 levels. A huge multi-storey mill was built at Ynys y Pandy SH550433, with extensive water courses and reservoir, workers housing and a railway to Porthmadog. In spite of this investment by 1859 its 200 men were producing under 1400 tons pa, a derisory 7 tons per man year. Peak output 1860, 2148 tons. Closed 1867, possibly with some subsequent sporadic working.

Remains At the quarry site there is a great deal of low grade rubbish and it is apparent that quarrying was tried and abandoned at a number of points, with bad-rock intrusions preventing orderly working. Four terraces were served by a single central incline, three levels above these seem not to have produced at all. There is a separate small level served by its own short incline, near the bottom of which was an underground trial (adit collapsed).

The 3′ tramway gauge was used on the inclines and on the working terraces, 2′g seems to have been also employed. Where the incline bridges the terraces there are differing sized apertures to suit the two gauges. There are some 2′g slate sleepers for Thomas Hughes rail.

There are several dressing sheds, blast shelters etc. on the worked levels. At ground level there is a possible barrack block and a stable. In this latter is a slate slab with 1″ dia holes, possibly for drill testing. There is a curious absence of weigh-houses and no obvious powder house.

About the site are several borings up to 3″ diameter and more, which on an unpowered site suggests the use of the 3 man operated Dixon drill.

The best known features is the curious overhanging curved wall retaining some of the huge quantity of bad rock that was extracted, from blocking the tramway.

The trackbed of the 3′ gauge tramway that took material to the mill passes a grove of trees, the site of the manager's house, behind are the vestiges of the 18 pairs of houses, (the village of Treforus) laid out in 3 "streets", which were built for the workforce. One can trace the covered leats that brought water for these dwellings and to the manager's house.

This trackbed continues to, and past the magnificent 3 storey Ynys y Pandy mill. From the mill the tramway can be traced almost without interruption to Porthmadog.

A piece of multi fish-belly rail acts as a gatepost at the Prenteg turning some ½ mile away, but this is unlikely to have been from the area, possibly original FR metal. (42)

HENDRE DDU SH519444

Pit. Originally a small early 19th C. unmechanised open working with material being directly carted away. Developed into a pit with tunnel access to a small mill and an incline down to the road. As work progressed requiring lower adits, a turbine powered mill, possibly of wood was built at foot of incline, 1861 60 men 700 tpa. Probably closed 1875 when reservoir dam collapsed. Material carted down valley, although at one time it was hoped to build a rail link to Cricieth.

Remains At, original, highest, level there are barracks with unusually tall windows, dressing sheds and a weigh-house. Below, a mill of unknown power source and a weighbridge. The incline which has several adits leading onto it is in fair condition, with a small reservoir alongside. Only the foundations remain of the roadside mill which may have been of wooden construction. On the old access track is a nice powder house.

In the main working is some tunnelling which may have been investigations. There are a number of other smaller workings nearby, some of which may have been productive. One was at one time used as reservoir. (11)

ISALLT SH532448

Open quarry operating around the 1840s-50s. Material lowered by incline to a working area where there may have been a mill. As working deepened, access was by tunnel. There may have been a tramway to the road.

Remains Very little apart from incline formation and some ruined buildings. At the higher level there is a surprisingly long tramway bed for tipping. Tunnel to sinc has collapsed.

The substantial and level construction of the access track suggests that it was, at least, intended as a tramway. (14)

LLAN Alternative name for Isallt.

MARINE TERRACE SH497378

Small open working.
Remains Vestiges behind houses. (3)

MOELFRE SH521451

A modest sized enterprise opened in the 1860s. An open pit working with material being taken first by cutting, then by tunnel and finally by uphaulage to an adjacent mill. Finished slate being taken down to the valley floor by incline. Later, a new, lower tunnel provided access and drainage, finished product being taken out through this and down a new incline to a mill on the valley floor. A second reservoir at lower level supplying this new mill. Finished product was carted down valley. About 30 men employed producing around 600 tons pa. Closed about 1880.

Remains Not an easy site to "read" as besides new work overlaying older operations, a gallery leading out of one of the pits may have been a pre-existing copper mine, the access road to the site was diverted and extended to serve an early 20th C. quartz working. On that track are two adits that may have been late attempts at underground quarrying.

Above the site is a reservoir and a powder house and another building that pre-dates the quarry operation. There are two pits, (one water filled), linked part way down by a cutting. At this level the dry pit has the remains of a water-wheel powered chain incline with a stone lined tailrace. Iron fixing bolts show where a launder may have fed this wheel. The tailrace leads down to a working area with mill, weigh-houses etc. A nearby tunnel also connects to this same pit. Not far away another tunnel connects to the "wet" pit at present water level.

At the base of the dry pit a section of the pit side has been elaborately walled and carries a fine stone cantilevered stairway, there is a lined tunnel, now obviously blocked, leading to the "wet" pit which not only drained that pit, but also provided access.

A second tunnel drains and provided access to the dry pit after the upper mill was abandoned.

One can see where the original incline has been tipped over and from the new, lower reservoir a stone line leat actually goes between the pillars of the drumhouse of the incline down to the lower mill, from where it continues to launder pillars leading to the site of a large overshot wheel. This lower mill is in reuse and has, in the river, the remains of a small undershot wheel.

It is of note that there are 2 disused and one active water turbines on the site, all of course post-dating the quarrying. The earliest, which is said to be an ex Hendre Ddu item was fed by a diversion of the water-wheel leat, the second by an iron pipe and the one now in generating use, by plastic piping. (12)

MOEL LEFN SH548483, 550489 and 551488
Probably trials only.
Remains Tiny buildings on first two sites, rubbish runs. (23)

MORFA LODGE SH567386
Said to be a very small working circa 1880.
Remains Area built up. (39)

MOEL Y GEST SH559388
Putative site.
Remains Some possible old workings. Not to be confused with later stone quarry near top of the hill (with incline). (32)

MYNYDD EDNYFED SH507394
A pit working producing a poor product, on the western extremity of the slate area. Possibly 1840s, closed by 1880.
Remains No buildings some pits and rubbish runs. The access track now forms the road to the Golf Club and can be traced across the course. (5)

PENCRAIG SH519393
Very small pit.
Remains Development obscures site. (10)

PENNANT VALE = Dolgarth and Dol Ifan Gethin.

PENMORFA SH552408
Hillside quarry with incline that crossed but did not connect to the Gorseddau tramway. Operated from 1820s to 1870s.
Remains Incline and excavation, remains of a mill etc., powering of which is unclear. (27)

PENRHYNLLWYD SH559393
Putative site, possibly not slate.
Remains Ground disturbance. (33)

PENYBANC SH562372/562374
Very small open workings. Possibly block for building, circa 1870s.
Remains Slight depressions in ground. (35)

PONT RHYD GOCH SH394407
Putative slate site.
Remains Some scratching here that might have been quarrying. (1)

PRINCESS SH553495
A small and remote hillside working of 1880s as extension of Prince of Wales, with some attempt at underground operation. Material was carried down to Prince of Wales.
Remains Some ruined dressing sheds and other buildings. At a lower level an adit from which apparently no useable product was taken. The track down to Prince of Wales quarry is traceable. Evidence of Thomas Hughes rail. (28)

PRINCE OF WALES SH549498
An old open working, finished product being carried to Rhyd Ddu. Some development in the 1860s when possibly three levels were worked. Vigorously opened in 1873 when the extension of the Gorseddau Tramway to the site gave ready access to Porthmadog. Further levels were started, connected by a single main incline to give seven in all. Some underground working took place on three levels.

A water powered mill was built at the then new terminus of the Gorseddau reached from the foot of the main incline by an elevated tramway and a second short incline. At the peak 200 men were employed producing 5000 tons pa. Closed 1886, but some small scale working up to 1920. All reduction of roofing slate took place on the terraces, slab only being dealt with in the mill.

Remains On each working level there are a number of buildings with dressing sheds etc. one of them having a particularly fine rake of such sheds and a barrack block without fireplaces (possibly portable stoves used). There may have been steam sawing on one terrace. The well engineered incline has remains of its final, upper drumhouse and traces of the two earlier drumhouses that were abandoned as incline was extended upwards.

As the working was to the east of the incline and much tipping to the west, the incline bridges a number of rubbish runs.

On the lowest working level is evidence of some underfloor leatwork. Some adits are open, leading to very limited chambering.

The little building behind the reservoir, was the workshop possibly a reuse of a pre-existing structure.

The stretch of level tramway past the reservoir is a prominent feature as is the lower incline drumhouse. One can see traces both of work begun to raise the height of the dam and the formation of a little tramway to serve that work. The lower incline to the mill is much degraded.

The small mill with wheelpit alongside, has very pleasing archways. There is a row of launder pillars adjacent.

The trackbed of the tramway to the south has some interesting little bridges and embankments and immediately to the north, on the subsequent extension to the Cwm Dwyfor mine, is a deep, curved cutting. (24)

PRINCE LLYWELYN SH518439

A small pit working, product being taken away by the Hendre Ddu track. Its late 1880s closure means that in spite of its size it outlasted almost all other quarries in this valley. Some authorities class this as an outliner of Hendre Ddu and apply the name Prince Llywelyn to that quarry.
Remains Pits and walling. Traces. (9)

TAN YR ALLT = Cwmbach.

TU HWNT Y BWLCH SH561389

A small and early working with cart access. Not to be confused with the later stone quarry which was connected to Porthmadog by tramway.
Remains Almost nothing, some traces of retaining wall for cart track. (34)

TY CERRIG SH550409

Working unlikely to have been slate.
Remains Excavation. (25)

TYDDYN LLWYN SH562386
Flooring flags produced in 1830s-40s?
Remains Almost none. (36)

TYDDYN MAWR SH506428
Tiny open quarry.
Remains Excavation only. (4)

TY'N Y LLAN SH554406
Hillside quarry connected by incline to Gorseddau tramway. Unlikely to have been slate.
Remains Excavation and incline. (30)

YMLYCH SH508407
Small hillside working. 1840s?
Remains Shallow pit. (6)

YNYSCYNGAR SH554365
Putative but improbable quarrying site, highly unlikely that slate was won here, but it was certainly the principal shipping point for the area before Porthmadog was built.
No remains. (29)

YNYS Y PANDY SH550433
This unique, cathedral-like structure follows the pattern of many mid-Victorian industrial buildings (such as the Cannons Road Gasworks, Bristol). Built in the mid 1850s to serve Gorseddau Quarry, it was out of use by the late 1860s, but was occasionally used later as a public hall.
The roof and upper floors are gone, but the stonework has been conserved by the Snowdonia National Park. It contains an obvious wheelpit for a breastshot wheel with a very deep shafting pit and a fine "walk in" water tunnel linking with the traceable leat from Llyn Cwmystradllyn. Alongside the wheelpit, below the working level a workshop can be identified. There is a trench at the end of the mainshaft pit to allow the shaft to be withdrawn for repair.
The tramway appears to lead by an embankment to an upper level and leave at ground level, suggesting some kind of gravity assisted work-flow, but the possibility of using saws on even as massive a wooden floor as this apparently had, is questionable. There would have been no trimming, the mill dealing exclusively with slab work. The small amount of waste indicates that total output was trifling. (26)

YNYSTOWYN SH572385
Putative, but highly improbable location.
Remains Nothing identified, possibly could have been some rock exposed when the cob was built. (40)

YSGUBOR GERRIG SH510427
Tiny scratching circa 1880.
Remains Possible ground disturbance. (7)

Glasllyn Section 7
Croesor, Beddgelert and District

General

This area comprises the quarries that were in the Glaslyn valley or whose transport routes led through it.

Some were open workings but most were underground.

The majority of sites were small and many, particularly around Beddgelert, were tiny emphemeral undertakings, little more than trial burrowings, searching for virtually non-existant rock.

Hafod y Llan was more substantial and has interesting remains, especially its incline system.

Some in the Nantmor area were on a reasonable scale with a degree of mechanisation.

It is in the larger of those that worked the western end of the Ffestiniog veins that the most interest lies, Rhosydd, Pant Mawr, Fron Boeth and, to a less extent Parc, are among the most archaeologically important remains extant.

Transport

Numerically, most of the quarries produced such little product as to make no demands on any system of transport.

Portrheudden was, up to the end of the 18th C., virtually on the Glaslyn estuary. Others could cart or carry to the estuary, or later, to Porthmadog, around 1850/60 Rhosydd carted or packhorsed down Cwm Orthin to the Ffestiniog Railway. There are discernable tracks down Cwm Croesor (below the more modern road to the quarry) and down Cwm Maesgwm. Road improvements in the mid nineteenth C. between Llanfrothen and Penrhyndeudraeth, were possibly due to the requirements of Croesor quarry.

Railways for the area had been mooted during the latter decades of the 19th C., the slate quarry traffic that would arise from the Beddgelert area being often cited in proposals, but by the time the Welsh Highland Railway opened in 1923 such quarrying as had been there had ceased.

The one rail link actually built was the most notable 2'g. Croesor Tramway of 1864, Horsedrawn, it linked to Porthmadog, the Rhosydd, Croesor, Fron Boeth, Parc and other minor quarries. It operated until the mid 1930s and never being officially closed, unofficial use in Cwm Croesor itself may have continued into the 1950s.

The line is traceable throughout its length. It starts at the head of Cwm Croesor with the spectacular Rhosydd and Croesor inclines, the highest

SECTION 7: GLASLYN

HORSE/GRAVITY
TRAMWAY (DISUSED).

NARROW GAUGE
STEAM RAILWAY (DISUSED).

single pitch inclines in the industry. The former connected to its quarry by a magnificently engineered formation.

It reached the valley floor via the nice Blaen y Cwm Incline which has the pipes of the Croesor quarry power station alongside.

Part way along the valley floor it met the foot of the Pant Mawr/Fron Boeth incline. This incline was originally in 2 pitches, from the top of which it connected to Pant Mawr quarry by another finely engineered tramway.

In about 1886 when the Fron Boeth quarry was much developed as a downwards extension of Pant Mawr, the upper pitch was abandoned and the lower pitch extended upwards some 100'. From this new incline head a line ran down valley to a tunnel (now blocked near the north western end) into Cwm Maesgwm. This tunnel is unique to the industry.

Near Croesor village was a little feeder from the tiny Croesor Bach digging, and shortly after passing over the third of three most attractive bridges, it met the branch to Parc Slab quarry.

A fine stone embankment led to the top of the two-pitch Parc incline. The lower drumhouse is ruined, but the upper one has been converted into a house.

Near the foot of these inclines was the Parc quarry branch junction, from there the formation runs across level ground to join the clearly defined route to Porthmadog, which was reused by the Welsh Highland Railway.

1.	SH571485	Meillionen
2.	573409	Portreuddyn (old site)
3.	578408	Portreuddyn (new site)
4.	579466	Cwm Cŷd
5.	579472	Cwmcloch
6.	579409	Fron Oleu
7.	580420	Vron
8.	582420	Aberdeunant
9.	582468	Goat
10.	584476	Bronhebog
11.	584496	Gwernlasteg
12.	594453	Dinas Ddu
13.	598394	Braich Gwilliad
14.	599514	Cae'r Gors
15.	605466	Cwmcaeth
16.	611458	Dolfriog
17.	613524	Hafod y Llan
18.	616421	Brondanw Isaf
19.	619426	Brondanw Uchaf
20.	620426	Brongarnedd
21.	626436	Parc
22.	629481	Berthlwyd

23.	631484	Gerynt
24.	632436	Hafoty
25.	635445	Garreg Uchaf
26.	632444	Parc Slab
27.	632490	Blaen-nant
28.	632499	Castell
29.	634437	Bryn y Gelynen
30.	633433	Llidiart yr Arian
31.	637452	Croesor Bach
32.	637457 etc.	Criblwyd
33.	637463	Gelli
34.	638418	Hafod Boeth
35.	643434	Hafod Uchaf
36.	643462	Cnicht
37.	646448	Cefn y Braich
38.	647446	Fron Boeth Tunnel
39.	651485	Llyn Llagi
40.	652448	Fronboeth
41.	657457	Croesor
42.	658446	Pant Mawr
43.	658476	Cwm y Foel
44.	659458	Upper Croesor
45.	664461	Rhosydd
46.	680493 & 681488	Cwm Fanog

ABERDEUNANT SH582420
Possible site.
Remains Lost in forestry. (8)

ABERGLASLYN = Cwm Caeth.

BERTHLWYD SH629481
Pit working, operated on two levels with inclines. Reduction in a small mill area. Active in 1860s/70s, employed about 30 men, output about 170 tons pa. Cart access, may have used Croesor tramway.
Remains Little on site itself, there is a very fine, though ruinous, house, there are some other buildings, one converted into a dwelling. (22)

BLAENANT SH632490
Possible trials.
Remains Traces of excavation. (27)

BRAICH GWILLIAD SH598394?
Putative site.
Remains Nothing traceable. (13)

BRAICH Y PARC = Cefn y Braich.

BRONDANW ISAF SH616421
Tiny open quarry, said to have employed 10 men at one time producing 60 tons pa. Operated in early 1820s. Slate quality described as poor. Access direct to road.
Remains Base of possible dressing shed. (18)

BRONDANW UCHAF SH619426
Extremenly small. Said to have employed 5 men in 1836. Material taken down a slide to the road.
Remains Excavation and vestiges of slideway. (19)

BRONGARNEDD SH620426
Small pit. Said to have employed 10 men around 1820 producing 70 tons pa. Crude incline or slide to road.
May be same as above.
Remains Traces of incline? (20)

BRONHEBOG SH584476
Small underground working.
Remains Four collapsed adits, vestiges of buildings, site now heavily overgrown. (10)

BRYN Y GELYNEN SH634437
Small open pit working from about 1860, 5 men employed.
Remains Traces of dressing sheds. (29)

CAE'R GORS SH599514 etc.
This was a series of small underground workings made in the mid 1870s which produced little product, failing to fulfill the expectations that this area then promised.
Remains At location above, a collapsed adit a dressing shed and a tiny shelter with shelf. At 594512, collapsed adit and nearby a most curious keyhole plan underground shelter. The circular portion 2.5m dia is vaulted over and the 0.5m wide x 3m long 'tail' is covered over with slab. Purpose unknown. At 593516 collapsed adit and tiny half-underground shelter. At 592519 Collapsed adit and vestige of a tiny shelter. Trimming waste of good quality on the ground in small quantities each location. (14)

CASTELL SH632499
An underground working certainly 18th cent. Possibly much older.
Remains Adit slant collapsed, quite extensive rubbish runs on the opposite side of the road. (28)

CEFN Y BRAICH SH646448

Hillside terraces, in 1877/83 about 20 men employed, 240 tons pa. Product described as brittle. Became part of Pant Mawr/Fron Boeth in 1857, two open workings being designated levels 19 and 20.
Remains Working faces and tramway formations connecting to Fron Boeth incline system. (37)

CEUNANT PARC = Parc.

CNICHT SH643462 etc.

An underground working most spectacularly located some 800' above the valley floor. Two adits, the westerly one being reached by a zig-zag path with a possibility that a ropeway may have been used to lower material. The easterly adit may have had some simliar access but material seems to have been carried part way down, then lowered on a slideway, continuing to valley floor by a path, possibly man carried.

Understandably there were several attempts to reach the slate from the other side of the hill but none of these seems to have been successful. Operating in 1860s with 6 men employed producing 20 tons pa. Certainly worked earlier and probably attempted to be worked later.

Remains Both adits are open. The slideway from the eastern adit is a prominent feature, but any track has virtually disappeared. Much of the track up to the western adit remains, eroded and partly scree covered. There is a tiny dressing area with ruins of a shed outside this adit and some 6m below is a substantial platform that appears to have been a stocking area and landing platform either for loading pack animals or for a ropeway. Both here and near the dressing shed are a number of slates, mostly doubles with some ladies and a few singles. Both adits are open, but only go a short distance.

Below almost at valley floor level are some building ruins possibly not connected with the quarry. If a ropeway was used this would have been the lower termination and possible base blocks can be seen. (36)

CRAIG BOETH = Gelli.

CRIBLWYD SH639460, 637457 & 639460

Abortive underground trials.
Remains Both adits are open to dead headings, the southerly one ending in a face partially drilled for shot firing, possibly attempts to reach the Cnicht slate by an easier route. Also collapsed adits at 631454, 632457, 634457. (32)

CROESOR SH657457

A medium sized underground quarry, unusual in never having had any significant surface workings, in employing forced ventilation, in the number of, for its size, steam engines used, the ingenuity of its engineering and in the small volume of its rubbish tips (due to a vigorous policy of backfilling worked out chambers).

Working the western limits of the Blaenau Ffestiniog slate with mixed fortune from the 1850s, closing in 1878. Re-opened in the 1895 under the energetic management of Moses Kellow, producing 5/6000 tons pa, but declined rapidly during the early years of the century. Finally closed 1930.

The water powered mill, (28' wheel) with about a dozen saws was built in the early 1860s. A 1866 extension with 12-14 saws had a 39' wheel operating totally underground from the tailrace of the first, with 13hp steam back-up. Shafting was underfloor with an underfloor rubbish tramway. The water wheels were replaced by Kellow with a Pelton wheel, driving through overhead shafting. All electrified later.

Underground working was arranged on seven levels or floors. At the far end of the access tunnel (floor A) an incline went up the vein to floors B, C and D Up and another incline going down to floors B and C Down, with a further incline joining C Down with D Down.

Several steam engines were used for pumping, ventilation and haulage and, at one time, a steam turbine (on level D Up). Much attention was given to ventilation, there were several vertical shafts out to bank, one being used to experiment with waterblast ventilation. A Guiblas fan was installed in 1866 and later a most impressive stone fan-house near the adit. It is believed that these vertical shafts were at one time used, via ropes and pulleys to water-balance a lower incline and to counterbalance the upper incline.

An attempt was made to drive a second adit direct to the lowest part of the workings but this was never completed. A hydro station was specially built to power the air drills for this development and a short external incline laid down for a counterbalance to haul out spoil.

In the mid 1890s compressed air drills were used, with a water powered compressor. Partially electrified in the late 90s, a full scale 350 kw ac hydro-electric plant was opened in 1904, with a small dc supply for excitation and for the manager's house lighting.

Electric locos were in use by 1905. Later two steam locos were used.

Finished product was originally carted to the Ffestiniog Railway at Penrhyndeudraeth, (the straight road beyond Garreg Llanfrothen was made by them) but after 1864 was taken down to the Croesor Tramway by an unusually long incline, (reducing the carriage cost from 7/10½ (39p) to 2/6½ (12.5p).

Remains As the workings were used for explosive storage up to the 1970s the condition of some parts is good, but it is flooded up to adit level.

Little remains of the mill etc. and nothing of the fine fan-house, the area having been cleared in the 1980s.

Immediately below the tip can be seen the small tip of the abortive second tunnel and near it the outline of the balance track. In the valley below, near the foot of the Rhosydd incline there are the traces of the small compressor house with some sign both of the pipe run to it and the air-pipe run from it. Above, on the hill there are traces of the vertical shafts and an extensive leat system. The filling of the feed dam has been washed out. The ledge for the leat and a gully for later pipework may be seen.

Underground the 440 yard long access tunnel is of unusually large bore, part way along at least one of the vertical shafts above is passed. At the far end it widens into a large marshalling area. There are several buildings and artifacts associated with the later storage function. The incline down is flooded up to adit level and the massive masonry of the haulage winch installed for explosives handling, hinders access to the incline up. To the right is a large flooded chamber, with a collapsed bridge to workings beyond. To the left are two blind tunnels.

Near the adit, the incline with ruined drumhouse is a prominent feature, it being second in vertical extent only to the adjacent Rhosydd incline.

The power station building is intact and in reuse near the foot of the Blaen y Cwm incline of the Croesor Tramway and the feed pipe from Llyn Cwm y Foel is largely intact. (41)

CROESOR BACH SH637452

A small underground working and although quite late (1866/8) was unmechanised, hand dressing being done in shelters adjacent to the adit. Said to have employed 12 men but only produced 40 tons pa. A short tramway led to Pont Sion Goch, where slate was loaded onto the Croesor Tramway.

Remains Adit collapsed, ruins of dressing sheds, tramway formation traceable, slate waste on ground at Croesor Tramway loading point. Three other trial adits are on the hillside above. (31)

CWMCAETH SH605466

A small open working possibly 1870s, material reduced in a small water powered mill. Material carted to Nantmor village. Said to have employed about 12 men and have been working 1876-79

Remains Tunnel into pit. Several buildings, but these have been much altered for agricultural reuse. (15)

CWMCLOCH SH579472

Tiny underground working, undoubtedly unsuccessful.

Remains Collapsed adit, ruins of one small building, traces of an access track. (5)

CWM CŶD SH579466

Almost certainly an unsuccessful trial.

Remains Collapsed adit. (4)

CWM FANOG SH680493 & 681488
Possible site of trials.
Remains Nothing other than possible slight excavation. (46)

CWM Y FOEL SH658476
Small underground working on an inaccessible site. Said to have been employing 5 men in 1820s producing 20 tons pa. Finished product possibly man carried down Cwm Croesor.
Remains Collapsed adit. (43)

CWM Y LLAN Earlier, upper workings of Hafod y Llan.

DINAS DDU SH594453
Small hillside quarry with some underground workings. It had a small tramway network and a water powered mill. Slate carted to Porthmadog.
Remains A residence occupies what was possibly the site of an office or other building. The Mill with its wheel-pit has been used as a source of stone for nearby farm structures. There is some leatwork. A nice stone cutting leads to the working area. Adit open, but only goes a short distance. (12)

DOLFRIOG SH611458
Open pit, stated as active 1865 with 10 men producing 40 tons pa.
Remains Virtually nothing, site in forestry. (16)

DORLLAN DDU = Cae Gors.

FRON BOETH SH652448
Underground, a costly and ambitious 1886 enterprise to extend and develop the Pant Mawr workings.
Three adits to chambers developed below the Pant Mawr workings were served by a short single acting table incline which brought material down to a steam powered mill. Finished product was taken along a contour chasing incline to the head of a long, stone embanked incline. From the foot of this incline a 500 yard tunnel led to Cwm Croesor, where the line turned up valley to a point above the head of the lower pitch of the Pant Mawr incline. This lower pitch being extended (and the upper pitch abandoned).
In the early 1890s a further mill was built at the tunnel entrance possibly to deal with Cefn y Braich material, and in anticipation of downward development. This mill was nominated as Level 22 (in a continuation of the Pantmawr and Moelwyn numbering sequence).
Remains The upper mill (Level 18) has evidence of 3 saw-tables and 3 dressing machines having been installed although the building is large enough for twice this number. Alongside the mill is a large Lancashire boiler which must have been originally taken up via the Pant Mawr

inclines and possibly was originally installed in the Pant Mawr mill.

The single acting table incline seems to have been a water balance, in which case it would have been originally a Pant Mawr item predating the actual Fron Boeth development. There is, running alongside it, a slate lined channel.

There are various buildings on site and, part way along the tramway, the foundations of an elevated office structure.

There are a number of adits, some blocked, some wet, leading to chambering working rather poor rock. There is much backfilling, including some in the adits.

The drumhouse and incline (which also served the Cefn y Braich workings) down to the lower mill are in good condition but the lower mill itself is very ruinous. (40)

FRON BOETH TUNNEL SH647446

This tunnel is unique as, although tunnelling is implicit in most slate quarrying operations, this is the only one outside an actual quarrying site and is one of the longest tunnels ever cut for horse drawing.

Remains The tramway tunnel is penetrable from here as far as the collapse near the northern end. Most curiously there is some chambering work inside. Over the hill at the northern end the tramway up the Croesor valley can be followed to the head of the (extended ex Pant Mawr lower) incline. There is some brake gear in the drumhouse and some rope-rollers on the ground. (38)

FRON OLEU SH579409

Tiny pit working. This may have been part of Portreuddyn, or a separate working.

Remains Excavation only. (6)

GARREG UCHAF SH635445

Tiny pit possibly never produced.

Remains Slight excavation. (25)

GELLI SH637463

A compact and isolated underground working seemingly operated as a "family business" with the owner living "over the shop". Finished product was carted to Croesor village.

Remains There are some small ruined buildings on the site, and some distance away a small dwelling that may have been connected with the quarry. However the main feature is the substantial house with workshops, including a smithy, in a lean-to at the rear. The workings, basically on two levels, can be entered. Above and behind the site is an adit, open, that seems to have been a trial only. The cart track is traceable. (33)

GELLIAGO Alternative name for Gerynt.

GERYNT SH631484
A moderate sized open pit working, material may have been raised by horse-whim. A gravity incline led down to a large water powered mill. Active around 1870 with 30 men employed producing 200 tons pa. Finished slate taken by wagon to Porthmadog, part of the journey possibly on the Croesor Tramway.
Remains There is a stone-built incline out of the pit but the method of haulage is unclear. There is an incline formation down to the mill, which has a wheelpit in the middle and launder pillars leading to it. A curious feature is the flight of steps in a passageway alongside the incline. There is a fine rubbish-retaining wall alongside the road. (23)

GOAT SH582468
An ephemeral underground working that may or may not have produced saleable slate.
Remains Two adits in tandem, the lower one certainly unproductive, both collapsed. Vestiges of an access track. (9)

GWERNLASTEG SH584496
Open quarry, opened in 1870s but not developed.
Remains Excavation and rubbish runs, traces of buildings, access track. (11)

HAFOD BOETH SH638418
This is a metal mine but there is a report of it being a slate operation employing 12 men producing 50 tons pa in the 1860s.
Remains Nothing that can be identified as slate working. It is possible that there is confusion between this site and Hafod Uchaf. (34)

HAFOD UCHAF SH643434
A compact underground working with several adits in a little valley, with a water powered mill. Operated in late 1870s with 12 men employed producing 60 tons pa. Material removed by cart.
Remains Adits collapsed, a small mill building with wheelpit, a nice forge and some other small structures. (35)

HAFOD Y LLAN SH613524
An open working believed to have been started in late 1840s but could be up to 30 years earlier. Considerable development in late 1870s in anticipation of a railway from Beddgelert to Betws-y-coed providing ready transport. It was at this time that the water-wheel powered mill seems to have been extended and converted to turbine operation. A system of tramways and inclines brought material to the mill and finished product was sent by a short tramway to the Cwm y Llan cart road which

served the copper mines. At the time of the big expansion this route was superceded by a tramway down to Pont Bethania of truly heroic proportions. From there, material was carted to the Croesor Tramway for conveyance to Porthmadog. Closed 1880s.

Remains The quarry site, which is on the Watkin path to Snowdon is unremarkable. There are a number of workings at several levels, dispersed over a wide area and connected by 2 inclines. There is an interesting archway where one tramway was carried over another and pieces of drilled slate seem to be slate sleepers. Lower down are the ruins of a number of buildings including the mill, clearly originally having a water-wheel at one end, extended by building on the far side of the wheelpit and converting to turbine power. Some of the wheel launder pillars still stand, it is possible that a disused incline carried the turbine feedpipe. The original tramway now forms the path between the site and Gladstone rock.

The really notable feature is the later tramway. From the site is gradually descends for ¾ mile, via impressive stone embanking, cuttings and a rock-cut shelf to the head of the upper incline. On route it cuts an earlier tramway (which brought ore from the Braich yr Oen copper mine to the Llywedd Bach Mill), on which is to be seen the finest run of stone block sleepers in North Wales.

The precipitous upper incline has a ruined drumhouse with brakeman's hut. Part way down are the abutments of bridge where is crossed the cartroad.

From the foot of this incline the line runs for ¼ mile to a further drumhouse with hut at the head of the lower incline. A curious feature of this section is that it appears at first glance to run uphill.

The lower incline is shorter and also has traces of a bridge where it crossed the cart road and at its foot are the stables and sheds (now in reuse) for the carts used to convey slate down Nant Gwynant. (17)

HAFOTY SH632436

Open quarry operating around 1875/76 with 17 men producing 100 tons pa. Possibly had a water powered mill.
Remains Almost nothing site in forestry. (24)

LLIDIART YR ARIAN SH633433

Pit/underground. This early working was the precursor of Parc Slab quarry and this name was given locally to Parc Slab.
Remains Tramway to Parc Slab. (30)

LLYN LLAGI SH651485

A small and remote underground working apparently operating without any external buildings or shelter of any kind.
Remains Collapsed adits. (39)

MELLIONEN SH571485
Small underground working.
Remains Site now in forestry. Vestiges of a small building at collapsed adit. It is possible that a formation down the hillside was an incline. (1)

NAMOR This is probably Cwm Caeth quarry.

PANTILLAN Upper part of Porthrydyn.

PANT MAWR SH658446
Underground, sited some 1500 amsl. Operating in the 1840s in chambers under, communicating with, and with levels numbered sequentially with, the Moelwyn quarry on the other side of Moelwyn Mawr. From 1853 finished product was taken down on pack animal via Cwm Maesgwm to be loaded on the Ffestiniog Railway at Penrhyn. Later a small mill was built with incline connection. In 1863 there was a big development with a fresh incline to the mill being built, and partly using a pre-existing track, a spectacular tramway was constructed on a rock-cut shelf to the head of a two pitch incline down to the Croesor Tramway. A steam engine was installed in 1878.
Virtually all surface operations ceased in the 1886 when the workings were merged with the Fron Boeth undertaking.
Remains The inclines from the adits and the compact mill with its impressive retaining wall, and other buildings are to be seen, but the main feature is the tramway gently climbing round the shoulder of the hill to the top of the 1000 ft incline, the highest two pitch incline in any slate quarry system.
Several adits on various levels are penetrable to the chambering in the poorish, steeply dipping vein.
The drumhouse is very ruinous but the upper pitch can be followed down to the embanked inter-pitch manoeuvring loop. The original lower drumhouse obviously was demolished when the lower incline was extended to serve the Fron Boeth tunnel line but the "new" drumhouse is in fair condition with some of the gear in situ and there are rope-rollers on the ground. (42)

PARC SH626436
A compact underground operation in a narrow valley, opened around 1870. Material was brought from the adit to a water powered mill. Possibly used water powered haulage. Produced 351 tons with 15 men in 1883. Operated latterly in conjunction with Croesor.
Finished product, almost exclusively slab was taken by a short incline to a bridge across the Afon Croesor, then by a further short incline to make a junction with the Croesor Tramway at the foot of the Lower Parc incline. Closed 1920.
Remains Several buildings âre in reuse or in good condition and the

unusually ornate manager's house is still occupied. The river is so extensively bridged by massive slabs as to be virtually culverted. At the north eastern end of the site is a building with a wheel-pit and a slate bedded incline with rope-score marks, and a flight of stone steps alongside, this would seem to have been an uphaulage. The building contains a compressor base and offcuts suggest that the further building was an 'ornamental' department. All water powered.

Opposite is the collapsed adit which led to extensive underground chambering, nearby is a lavatory and the ruins of the main mill which was powered by a launder from the tailrace of the upper wheel. There is another building, now in reuse and a very extensive stocking area. There are massive rubbish runs.

At a higher level is a blocked adit which seems to have served purely for rubbish disposal.

Save for vestiges of the drumhouses, the tramway branch has been almost obliterated. (21)

PARC (SLAB) SH632444

A small working pit, with a sawing mill. Finished product being taken away on a branch of the Croesor Tramway which joined the main line near Croesor village. In 1870 20 men employed. Like the Parc quarry this was operated in conjunction with the Croesor quarry.

Remains Pit, accessed by a nice cutting, incline to mill site, foundations of mill building (present road cut through mill). On the other side of the road is an unusually large wheelpit, building remains and extensive rubbish runs. (26)

PORTREUDDYN (Old site) SH573409

Open quarry, 18th C. took slate, perhaps by horse sledge, to a shipping point near the present main road which represents the limit of the tidal estuary prior to the building of the Cob in the early 1800s.

Remains Working and rubbish runs, building that may not have been part of the quarry. (2)

PORTREUDDYN (New site) SH578408

This working which dates from the mid 19th C. possibly went partly underground. Material was taken by incline to a water powered mill near the road. Later owing to restricted water supplies, steam was used. Output presumably carted to Porthmadog. Ceased around 1870.

Much of the product was, more accurately Tremadoc Grit, a very hard rock used for slab especially steps (e.g. main entrance Plas Tan y Bwlch).

Remains There is, apart from the digging itself, some walling and a possible adit. The incline is much collapsed but at its foot is an unusual mill building, now in reuse, with a wheelpit and stone lined leat.

There are other buildings in this area in reuse including one that may have been the steam powered mill. (3)

RHOSYDD SH664461

Started in 1830s with small hilltop surface workings, developed underground from the 1850s until with 14 levels and 170 chambers it became one of the largest underground quarries outside Ffestiniog itself, producing in 1883 5616 tons with 192 men. There were 24 saw-tables and 24 dressing machines, the first saws having been run in 1854.

Initially, surface then underground, working progressed northwards, with at first dressing sheds, then mills being erected on an increasing scale as far down as level 9 where the final, major surface works were sited. This level became the main adit with a half mile long tunnel providing the main access and drainage. Levels below 9 were pumped and uphauled. Much use was made of water power for pumping, hauling, electric generation and air compression as well as for mill power. (Including reputed use of a Tom & Jerry machine). Being elevated (1700′ amsl) and with a poor catchment meant using an extensive leat system with several reservoirs to collect and store the water. Besides the surface reservoirs several old chambers were used for waste storage.

The site being remote meant that many of the men (and families) lived on or near the site (with their own chapel).

At first transport was difficult, material being sent by pack horse via Moelwyn and later by cart or sledge via Cwm Orthin. After 1864 the finely engineered tramway to the head of Cwm Croesor and the splendid incline down to the Croesor Tramway was used. Final closure in 1930.

Remains From the two pits to the south (the surface near the eastern one showing signs of the 1900 collapse) the dressing sheds, other buildings including mills, inclines, adits, shafts and so on follow a chronological order northwards. In the West twll is a winder. Immediately northward is 2 Level adit and an early mill and workshops. Beyond, at 3 level, is the "square" mill, above which can be seen the depression for the flat rods that carried motion from this 3 mill to a pump in the East twll. There is also the pit of a haulage wheel. Further on is 4 mill, offices, workshop and a lavatory.

Inclines lead down to the big mill area at 9 level. Like the other 3 mills, the big main mill here has now almost vanished. From its wheelpit part of the culvert that led away the tailrace under the working area is traceable. There are numerous other buildings, some with exceptionally nice windows and other detail. The 'street' of barracks is notable.

Near the 9 adit is the pit for the backshot wheel (and some fragments of that wheel), which powered the endless rope haulage system, which pulled wagons along the adit. There are also parts of trucks including a gripper truck that towed the journeys of trams.

Underground, at the far end of the adit is the sheave for this system.

The westerly workings may be penetrated by the suitably experienced but the whole of the eastern part is dangerous. All workings below 9 level are flooded.

There are two fine mass-balanced table inclines (5-9 and 3-6) with headsheave, table and balance truck intact. There is much track and pipework and many other artifacts, including bridges (all of which are dangerous). Also may be seen the inclined tunnel running up from 9 level which carried a travelling water tank which originally acted as a balance for an uphaul incline below 9 level, connection being made by a rope and pulley system. This unusual device enabled hauling below drainage level with the tank discharging above drainage level.

Amongst the prominent surface remains is a big structure alongside the track down to Cwm Orthin which is an unfinished wheelpit. Near the foot of this track adjacent to the Conglog mill (Blaenau Ffestiniog area) is a row of Rhosydd dwellings and not far away, in trees, Plas Cwm Orthin, the manager's house. Part way down that valley is the ruined Rhosydd chapel. In the vicinity of the site, particularly to the north are a number of reservoirs and lakes with leat systems partly traceable, (a collapsed timber dam is notable).

The old track via Moelwyn may be followed and the later route via Cwm Orthin is obvious.

The most spectacular relic is the incline down to the Croesor Tramway and the well engineered tramway to its head. At almost 700' it is the highest single pitch incline in the Slate industry. Lack of space at the top of incline meant that the drumhouse is sited some 50' above, the brake having been controlled by wires. The brakeman's shelter and control wheel platform are to be seen. (45)

SOUTH SNOWDON = Hafod y Llan.

TY'N Y CHWAREL = Dolfriog.

UPPER CROESOR SH659458
Small working incorporated in Croesor 1866.
Remains None identifiable as destinct from Croesor work. (44)

VRON SH580420?
Tiny pit working possibly associated with one of the Portreuddyn workings.
Remains None identified. (7)

WERNCASDEG Probably Cae Gors.

Blaenau Ffestiniog Section 8

General

This compact area of Ordivician slate in five workable veins, includes some of the largest and most efficient workings in the industry, collectively, in the latter part of the 19th C., producing about one third of the entire Welsh output. Other than early work, all were underground.

They form, roughly, a semicircle around the town of Blaenau Ffestiniog, which grew out of a few isolated farmsteads, solely as a result of the quarry operations.

Two, Gloddfa Ganol and Llechwedd, as well as being working quarries, have parts open to the public, their visitor centres providing much of interest. A number of the other large quarries after a period of idleness, are being worked by modern untopping methods, unfortunately much to the detriment of the 19th C. relics.

Apart from the quarrying sites themselves, the town dominated by glowering cascades of waste, shows in the detail of many of its buildings, some fine examples of the slate workers' craft. The "Slate Workers" window in the parish church, being a unique tribute to that craft.

Transport

This area is synonymous with the Ffestiniog Railway and all the quarries had access to it. Prior to its 1836 opening slate was taken to quays on the Dwyryd, downstream of Maentwrog. Latterly much by cart, but originally on the backs of animals or even of men. From there it was taken in a fleet of small boats for offshore trans-shipment on to sea-going craft. Many of these quays, on either side of the river are extant.

The F.R. itself is too well known to require mention. Some quarries reached it by direct incline connection, others by two feeder tramways.

The Cwm Orthin tramway of 1850, may be traced from the mills area of that quarry via two inclines (Tan y Muriau and Village) and a fine embankment and cutting to Tanygrisiau, where it joined the F.R. In 1874 it was extended to Conglog quarry, the present valley track substantially using the formation.

The Rhiwbach tramroad of 1863 formation runs as a clearly defined path from the top of the Rhiwbach quarry incline, past Manod, Blaen y Cwm and Cwt y Bugail quarries, to the head of No. 3 incline above Maenofferen quarry. From the Maenofferen area No. 2 incline (which is still tracked) dropped down to Bowydd quarry. A short level run took it to the head of No. 1 incline which descended to join the F.R. at the present town car park.

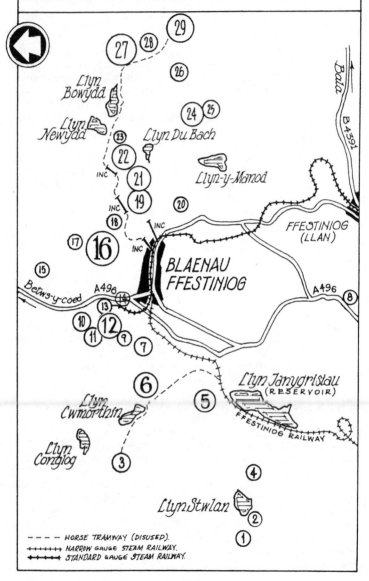

SECTION 8: BLAENAU FFESTINIOG

㉙
㉗ ㉘
㉖
Llyn Bowydd
㉔ ㉕
Llyn Newydd
㉓
Llyn Du Bach
㉒
㉑
Llyn-y-Manod
INC
⑳
⑲
INC
⑱
INC
⑰ ⑯
FFESTINIOG (LLAN)
⑮
Betws-y-coed
A496
BLAENAU FFESTINIOG
A496
⑧
⑭
⑬
⑩ ⑫
⑪ ⑨ ⑦
⑥
Llyn Cwmorthin
Llyn Tanygrisiau (RESERVOIR)
⑤
FFESTINIOG RAILWAY
Llyn Conglog
③
④
Llyn Stwlan
②
①

Bala
B 4391

- - - HORSE TRAMWAY (DISUSED).
+++++ NARROW GAUGE STEAM RAILWAY.
━┿━┿━ STANDARD GAUGE STEAM RAILWAY.

There are also the spectacular quarry inclines, such as the multi-pitched Moelwyn and Graig Ddu runs, and the single pitch, partly in tunnel, Wrysgan, all of which still make landscape features. The Llechwyd and some of the Oakeley inclines are decayed, but obvious, the Bowydd incline is a public path.

Llechwedd quarry, from 1879 and the Oakeley quarry from 1934 also used the L&NR (LMSR) at a loading point at Pant yr Afon. Product could either be loaded for rail distribution or for shipment at Deganwy (where there are still relics of the slate wharves). In the latter case, 2'g, wagons were entrained pic-a-back. This BR line is, of course, still in use.

The G.W.R. line of 1883 (still open to Trawsfynydd, but not then, as now, joined end on to the L&NWR). Using the trackbed of the Ffestiniog and Blaenau Railway, (1868) it could pick up slate, at Blaenau Ffestiniog, but also carried Graig Ddu wagons pic-a-back for loading onto the F.R.

The G.W.R. line south of Trawsfynydd closed in 1961, may be readily traced to the fine Cwm Prysor viaduct, where it was incorporated into the main road. From there it may be followed until its trackbed is drowned in the Trederwyn reservoir.

1.	SH656442 etc.	Bwlch Stwlan
2.	661442	Moelwyn
3.	670467	Conglog
4.	671446	Chwarel Twm Feltiwr
5.	676458	Wrysgan
6.	681459	Cwm Orthin
7.	689462	Nyth y Gigfran
8.	690421	Rhyd y Sarn (Mill)
9.	690466	Hollands
10.	693473	Welsh Slate
11.	694470	Gloddfa Ganol
12.	695470	Oakeley
13.	697469	Pant yr Afon (Sidings)
14.	697467	Glan y Don (Tip & Mill)
15.	699487 etc.	Ffridd y Bwlch
16.	700470	Llechwedd
17.	704473	Owain Goch
18.	706465	Votty
19.	708464	Bowydd
20.	709454	Pant y Rhyn (Mill)
21.	712463	Diffwys (Casson)
22.	714465	Maenofferen
23.	718467	Hysfa
24.	724454	Graig ddu
25.	725452	Manod ("Old" Manod)
26.	732455	Manod (Bwlch y Slaters)
27.	734468	Cwt y Bugail

28.	735459	Blaen y Cwm
29.	740462	Rhiwbach

BLAEN Y CWM SH735459, 736459, 734464

Pit/Underground. Three distinct workings, the earliest dating from before the 1820s. Much developed during the 1870s when the presently extant mill was built (water powered with steam back-up?), and the powered incline connection to the Rhiwbach Tramway made. The underground work lower down the site to the east does not seem to have been successful.

Prior to the use of the tramway via Blaenau Ffestiniog, material was carried via Cwm Machno to Trefriw. Closed around 1914.

Remains The main feature is the mill which has a very large wheelhousing at one end with access provided by cantilevered steps, and a fine tailrace tunnel. At the opposite end is an engine house and coal store and nearby are the vestiges of a portable engine boiler and firebox. There are possible rope apertures in, and pulley support pillars near, the engine house.

The mill waste chutes along one side are nicely constructed of slate and they feed into an unusually deep rubbish wagon run, which is bridged at intervals by slate slabs. There are several buildings, weigh-houses etc. and some artifacts including the upper sheave of the exit incline. This incline also goes down towards the abortive underground working (some small buildings and a flooded adit) but although there are rope markings indicating use, it does not run all the way to the adit area.

There is a lavatory block that appears to be built over a large pit. This is undoubtedly the wheelpit of an earlier mill. There are several other buildings, weigh-houses etc. in this area, and a little way off to the south, a possible powder-house. Above the site was a small reservoir formed by pounding behind the Rhiwbach Tramway formation.

A tunnel leads to a pit, apparently formed by untopping chambers. Curiously, this pit has a self-acting incline down into it, with a weigh-house at the head, apparently to provide through access from the working to the south east. This part of the site has been disturbed by recent operations, there are the foundations of a possible mill and a (blocked) tunnel under the Rhiwbach tramway. To the south west is a further pit working, access by a (flooded) tunnel. (28)

BOWYDD SH708464

A late 18th C. working substantially developed in the 1830s, after amalgamating to form the big Votty and Bowydd quarry, producing in 1882, 12092 tons with 344 men, with a peak output at the end of the 19th C. of over 17000 tons pa and employing nearly 500 men. One of the first quarries to use (hand) sawing. It was one of the earliest quarries to have an internal rail system (2.2″ g, 1825), latterly locomotive worked. Early user of Mathews dressers. Early user of circular saws (1827?). Early mill on 2 floors?

Ultimately there were three mills plus a writing slate factory, using water in tandem with a total of 50 saw-tables and 50 dressing machines. The three big mills, with central wheel pits, on massive terraces, making successive use of water, were slightly unusual in that the line shafting was underfloor and the track for the waste wagons was inside rather than outside the buildings. Numbered, downward a, b and c, latterly only the c was used, diesel powered. Although electric power was brought in from Dolwen in 1899 extensive use was still made of water power including, in the 1930s, a hydrostat to raise water. Water balances were used (eg C-B & B-A) and there was a 3 track water haulage incline. In the early 1930s diamond tipped saws were used.

As with all the quarries in this area, material was at first carried for shipment near Maentwrog, it was not until 1854 that an incline made direct connection with the Ffestiniog Railway, shortly afterwards supplanted by the use of the No. 1 incline of the Rhiwbach Tramway. By 1880 most material was going out by a connection made partway down the Diffwys incline.

Taken over by Oakeley in 1933 it was finally closed in 1963. Untopping operations were started by the Llechwedd company in the 1980s.

It is said locally that in 1920 fire-setting was tried when removing an unusually hard section of rock. If so, this must be the very last time such a technique was used in Wales.

Remains Owing to untopping operations on the quarrying site and to landscaping operations lower down much was lost during 1980s.

There is an extensive network of tramway, some with track on the ground. At one point there is an interesting tunnel leading to a slate slab floored terrace with a guard rail made of haulage rope, this is the Cooke level, actually part of Maenofferen.

The big Tuxford haulage incline is just discernable. Some adits are open. A nice feature is "Quarry bank", the manager's house alongside the Rhiwbach No. 2 incline. At about this level are several other buildings including the remnants of the two-storey water powered writing slate factory. There are weigh-houses, inclines etc. The original 1854 incline has been lost in subsequent work but the connection to the Rhiwbach Tramway near the foot of No. 2 incline is obvious. There are a number of wagons of various patterns there.

In spite of clearance, the route from the lowest mill level to join the Diffwys incline is traceable. The Rhiwbach route to the head of No. 1 incline, down to Blaenau is well engineered with cuttings and embankments. The No. 1 incline itself is in good condition but the rock-cut remote drumhouse has been largely collapsed. The lower end of the Diffwys incline, below the 'junction' has been surfaced as a path. The drumgear is most unusual as it had a brake located between the two halves of the drum.

There are numerous other buildings including offices and loco sheds and much substantial revetment work to retain terracing and to hold back rubbish from adits and working areas.

At the top of the site the old Votty pit is flooded as a water source. (19)

BUGAIL Alternative name for older part of Cwt y Bugail.

BWLCH STWLAN SH656442 & 658442
Old outliners of Moelwyn (see Moelwyn). (1)

BWLCH Y SLATERS This is the local (and correct) name for Manod and New Manod.

CESAIL Old name of Hollands or Upper quarry.

CHWAREL SION LLWYD Original part of Moelwyn.

CHWAREL TWM FELTIWR SH671446
Possible trial
Remains Traces of excavation. (4)

CONGLOG SH670467
A compact and delightfully situated quarry operating from 1874 to 1909 much of the time on a part-time basis. From adits high up (1425′ amsl) at the head of Cwm Orthin a short incline brought material to a small water powered mill. Finished product removed by tramway, via Cwm Orthin quarry. In its later days it was operated by two brothers, Rhosydd workers, they banked with a friend at Tan y Grisiau, who absconded with many years profits!
Remains The 2 adits are open (chambered out to bank) and the incline is obvious. The drumhouse has been extended in a curious manner. A leat, (was partly laundered in the quarry area), runs alongside the Rhosydd track.
The cottages alongside the mill were Rhosydd property as was the nearby house and, of course, the chapel. The Conglog mill itself has been substantially adapted for agricultural use but the wheelpit and launder pillars are extant. The tramway is readily traceable. (3)

CWM ORTHIN SH681459
A substantial underground enterprise that was notorious for bad working conditions. Opened in 1810 as an open quarry it was worked sporadically until the early 1860s when the tramway connection to the Ffestiniog Railway, justified substantial underground development.
Original chambering was above the water table with material being brought out by adits to mills at lake level. As work progressed deeper, pumping and haulage were called for, at first steam, later electrically powered. Output in 1882 was 10376 tons, with over 500 men employed.

The 3 mills, one steam, 2 water powered, contained up to about 50 saws and 50 dressing machines. After a serious collapse in 1884 production was much reduced. In 1900 it was incorporated into Oakeley quarry and all surface works abandoned. In 1925 there was a big scheme to develop open workings involving a new incline, powder house and the refurbishing of a mill and of the tramway, but this was abandoned. (Although untopping work was eventually commenced in the mid 1980s.) There was a fresh period of activity in the 1930s mainly underground and some further open working was done in the 1950s, all work ceasing by the 1960s. During the early 1980s it was worked underground on a very small scale, with a saw-table etc. underground and transport by Land-Rover. In the late 1980s more extensive untopping work commenced with a rebuilt mill. Until 1902 finished product was sent out by the two inclines of the Cwm Orthin Tramway.

Remains The most prominent feature is the main incline with its two drumhouses with some gear intact. One drum is unusual in having replaceable cast-iron segments on its brake ring. Nearby was the massive 1925 'Beau Geste Fort" powder house (tipped over 1990). There are various buildings on the several rubbish terraces which have been cut by a 1950s road.

At the northern end at lake level is the very ruinous Lake mill (latterly steam powered), Cwm Orthin House, the tree protected manager's residence and other buildings including weigh-houses, a small barracks, housing (there were some 30) and a stable (now in reuse). There are, in this area the formations of several inclines including two emerging from underground, with haulage engine bases at their heads. There are several adits including one with a chimney intended to carry away fumes from a steam winder inside. Underground the lower workings are flooded but above water level, there are inclines and chambers in some abundance, but the workings to the south are unsafe. Until the mid 1980s it was possible to pass through to Oakeley by the partly wooden floored connecting tunnel, which also served as a drainage tunnel.

Near the southern end of the lake with its obvious rubbish tippings, is the main barracks block (the early end, built of country rock has fallen but the later end, built of slate off-cuts, stands), and the ruinous 'Tiberias' chapel. The Lake incline down to main mills level also carried Conglog traffic. At the foot of incline is the Cross mill, (built in 1855) much degraded but with its central wheelpit obvious, (partly rebuilt 1989).

A little further south along the stacking yards are the ruins of the Lower or London mill built in three separate halls. The very deep wheelpit can be seen, the waterwheel drove the line shafting by chain. The wheel was replaced by a Pelton wheel, (removed 1989). All this area was much disturbed by late 1980s operations.

There is a nice feed-leat and holding pond. In this area the river is channelled by some very fine stonework but much of the bridging has collapsed.

On the hill above the site leats can be traced and one can see where the ground has sunk as a result of the underground collapse. Also to be seen are the cast iron markers defining the surface boundary between Oakeley and Cwm Orthin property.

The exit tramway is a delightful feature. (6)

CWT Y BUGAIL SH734468

A remote, partly underground quarry, an enlargement of the old Bugail working opened in the 1820s, it was developed following its connection to the Rhiwbach tramway in the 1860s at its peak producing over 3000 tons pa with well over 100 men, mostly living in barracks. Material was uphauled from two pit/underground workings to be reduced in a mill equipped with possibly as many as 20 saw-tables and dressing machines. Finished product going out on a branch of the Rhiwbach tramway. Water supply was minimal and was only used for cooling and for a waterbalanced incline. Steam powered the main inclines and the mill, replaced in the mill by an oil engine in latter years. Worked on a reduced scale until the 1960s.

Remains The principal feature is the mill, clearly much too large for the output of this quarry, constructed in three sections with a separate engine room. This building survived almost intact into the 1980s but is now very much collapsed. There are several other buildings on site including a workshop and, a little distance off near the tramway main line, a barracks. Overworking and erosion make this site unclear but near the mill is the head of what could be a waterbalanced incline with the trunk and the balance running on slightly different levels.

At the workings themselves a pleasing feature is a curved, rock-cut tunnel, which connects the two main working areas. Some traces of inclines etc. can be seen and there are remains of a steam winder. Some of the chambering is accessible. (27)

DIFFWYS CASSON SH712463 Also known as Diffwys.

The first organised quarry in the district, opened in the 1760s by Methusalem Jones of Nantlle who is said to have dug in this locality as a result of a dream. It covers a big area as much was originally pit worked, although some underground working may have been done as early as 1812. An early user of (hand) saws.

At first, sledgeways and packhorses were used to take material for shipment on the Dwyryd but in 1801 a cart road was built. A pioneer user of internal tramways, (originally 3'4½" gauge plateways, unique to the industry), and of internal inclines, some 9 being at one time in use. Later 2'2" gauge was used, the 3'4½" being retained for the trunks. This gauge difference may have accounted for their reluctance to use the Ffestiniog Railway, a reluctance demonstrated in 1845 by building the water powered Pant y Rhyn mill alongside their road. This was not their first mill, a small water-powered sawmill (later enlarged and converted to steam as No. 4 mill) slightly predated it. This possibly being the first

128

steam mill in the area. Their No. 6 steam mill of 1861 being the first integrated mill in the area. They used a unique type of trimmer, a big guillotine operated by an overhead crank from the line shafting.

They eventually connected with the F.R. in 1860 via the Bowydd incline (later to become No. 1 Incline of the Rhiwbach Tramway), but continued to cart for loading on the Dwyryd until the completion of their own direct incline to the F.R. in 1863.

The earliest, open, workings (Hen Gwaith) were at the top of the site with work more or less progressing downhill with some tentative underground working. Serious underground extraction started much lower down and this was followed by work, (Drum Boeth), higher up, close to the original diggings. In 1882 an entirely new underground venture, known as New Quarry was started, to the east of the site, was not successful.

By the early 1820s with a tonnage of well over 5000 pa it dominated the scene but by 1870/80 tonnage was only a little greater, with some 200 men. Declining towards the end of the century it continued on a small scale until about 1955. In the 1980s untopping work commenced by Greaves of Llechwedd.

Remains The site is now somewhat confused by the modern untopping work and the roads that have been constructed. Also, near the lowest part of the site, there is some intermingling with the Bowydd site, as this undertaking tipped to the south-east of Diffwys using a tramway that bridged the main Diffwys incline.

At the top of the site are some of the earliest buildings, weigh-houses etc. constructed of massive blocks of country rock in the traditional Meirionnydd manner. There are also several ponds and an interesting stone embanked leat and some tramway formations the old "wide" gauge slate sleepers. The original Hen Gwaith workings have been obliterated by the progression of the later Drum Boeth operations.

Nearby are the separate New Quarry workings with adits and some buildings and a tramway that leads, via two inclines and a narrow terrace through a tunnel (collapsed) to the upper mill. Near the lower of the two inclines is a fine flight of steps.

In the upper part of the quarry is a particularly interesting drumhouse, a conversion of a conventional self acting unit into a single acting powered table incline. The standard drum was shortened and supported by a third wall. A small working platform was sited alongside the end of the shortened drum, up under the eaves, to provide a housing for the electric motor and cramped space for the driver. This platform was reached by slate slab steps cantilevered out of the back wall. The brake, unusually was of a screw type. Lower down the site near the No. 6 mill is a similar drumhouse powering a railed haulage incline. It is a suite of buildings comprising a weigh-house and office as well as the drumhouse holding a shortened drum. The control/motor platform in this case was reached by an external stairway. The brake is an adaption of standard brake gear, but since the lever had to be shortened it is heavily weighed to assist application. There are still some rails on the crimp.

The No. 6 mill walls are in fair condition. The rubbish track alongside still has rail on the ground and a rubbish wagon in position. There are parts of guillotine type trimmers.

There are several other interesting drumhouses, one immediately below the upper mill is singularly massive. Another, which has a fine flight of steps nearby, has been converted into an office type building.

At the lower levels the original mill and other buildings have been covered by late untopping work.

There are many buildings and artifacts on this site, and the untopping operations, and in one case, a collapse, reveals the chambers and inclines (some with rail in situ). Some adits can be entered.

Landscaping in the mid 1980s obliterated much of the main incline but the drumhouse is extant incorporating a weighbridge (on the opposite side to the brakeman's cabin) and the drum had a central brake using automotive type linings. This incline also, by mid run hitching, served Bowydd, after its use by Diffwys was abandoned. The old 1800s road is still a road for much of its length and the upper part forms a natural access to the site. A number of the cottages in this area were built and owned by the quarry. The Pant y Rhyn mill still stands. (21)

FFRIDD = Blaen y Cwm.

FOTY Local correct spelling of Votty.

FFRIDD Y BWLCH SH699487, 700481, 701484 etc.
Small trials.
Remains Surface scratchings. (15)

FFRIDD Y GELLI Very early name for Maenofferen.

GLAN Y DON SH697467
Tip (and mill) for Oakeley reached by viaduct over Railway line.
Remains Tip has been levelled, viaduct pillars extant. (14)

GLAN Y PWLL = Nyth y Gigfran.

GLYN FFESTINIOG Early name for Conglog.

GRAIG DDU SH724454
Almost entirely open quarrying, the only one in the area.
A remote, elevated site suffering from considerable transport problems until the opening of the Ffestiniog and Blaenau Railway in 1868. Opened as Manod quarry around 1800 and developed as Graig Ddu in the 1840s. Due to water supply difficulties the mill had to be sited some distance

below quarry level and even then head could only be obtained by using a totally buried wheel with an iron lined underground leat.

In the 1880s there was a big mill development lower down hill again, a meagre supply being brought in from both north and south, the southern supply being assisted over rising ground by a pump operated by flat-rods from a water-wheel. The mill wheel was breast-shot partly buried, driving shafting under the mill. Later this shafting was extended to power a second mill and later again to power auxillary machinery. In the 1900s this wheel was replaced by a producer gas engine. The quarry was never electrified.

Although output was only some 3000 tons pa it was reported to have 36 saw-tables and 36 dressing machines on site. One mill converted to barracks.

Output in 1882 was 3140 tons with 110 men. Operations ceased in the 1940s but sporadic work on a small scale continued and in the 1980s untopping in conjunction with the Bwlch y Slaters site commenced.

After 1865 finished product was taken down to Tan y Manod by the grand 4 pitch, incline, notable for the unique use of the "Wild Cars" to convey men down after work. (In use up to 1946 closure.) After the conversion of the F & B Railway to standard gauge in 1883 the quarry trams were conveyed to Blaenau on pic-a-back rail trucks.

Remains This site is chiefly notable for the fine inclines. Due to later bulk working there is little to be seen on the quarry site itself, apart from tramway formations, some small building vestiges and an incline. There were several tunnels but these have now gone.

The incline down to the upper mills area is in fair condition but at Upper Mills level the almost unique underground wheel and water passages, the mills and other buildings, were tipped over by opencasting operations in the late 1980s.

There is a fine incline down to the Lower Mills level and part way down, to the north, is the stonefaced portal of a development tunnel 480 yards long, an unsuccessful attempt to reach the vein from below.

Lower Mills level (Lefl Ddu Oer) are the mills and other buildings. The low-level wheel pit and shafting tunnel, which contains some gearing, is to be seen. The leats and the pump-wheel pit are nearby.

There is a magnificent incline down to road level, with some wrecked wagons alongside it, including some placarded GWR.

The final incline, to the west of the road, down to the railway is less clear but its line is traceable. (24)

GLODDFA GANOL SH694470

(Or Middle Quarry) also known as Matthews. Part open, part underground, started in 1830 possibly on early workings by the Rhiwbryfdir Co. It lay between Hollands (Upper Quarry) and the Welsh Slate Co. (Lower quarry). Substantial underground working from 1840. Were pioneer users of trimming machines, (the Matthews Trimmer of

1852), and early users of steam for both mill power and for winding. A number of gravity and powered inclines were used, including one of six tracks, water balances were also used. Material went down by incline to the F.R. at Dinas. Became part of Oakeley in 1878. In 1882 (prior to the big fall of 1883) employed 362 men (a slight drop on the figures before amalgamation with Upper quarry) with an output of 13414 tons.

Name now used for the Mountain Tourist Centre on the site, which is also still a working quarry.

Remains See Oakeley. (11)

GREAVES = Llechwedd.

HAFODTY Old name for Votty.

HEN WAITH Early Diffwys development.

HOLLANDS SH690466

Cesail or Upper Quarry. Opened in 1827 by Samuel Holland the younger after he and his father disposed of their earlier lower workings to the Welsh Slate Co. It became a substantial undertaking with surface and, from 1840, underground working with inclines bringing material to surface. A steam powered mill, in use from about 1860, unusually, some gas lighting was employed underground (1850s). A notable feature was the 1000 yard long 'Horse Tunnel' which gave connection to the mill from the inclines down from above. 1882 output 13753 tons with 534 men.

An early user of the F.R. (1839), already having 2' g tramways throughout, material was lowered to it by a gravity incline. Became part of Oakeley Complex in 1878.

Remains See Oakeley. (9)

HYSFA SH718467

Very early 19th C. working.

Remains Possible excavation at edge of Diffwys. (23)

DAVID JONES Part of Maenofferen.

LLECHWEDD SH700470

This mainly underground quarry opened in the 1846, rapidly becoming one of the largest in the district, one of the most efficient in the Industry and a leader in methodology. E.g. the Greaves Trimmer of 1856 which became the standard machine in the Industry.

In 1882 24723 tons produced employing 553 men, this tonnage increasing in the 1890s. Up to 50 tons per man year were claimed, probably an Industry record, a 9-1 waste to make ratio was claimed against a local average of 12-1. Chambering went down almost to sea level with 20 miles of tunnels.

Highly mechanised mills were established from 1852, on several levels. Extensive use was made of water power for mill driving, pumping and haulage, both by water balance and direct cranking. There being a number of powered inclines, mostly underground and several gravity ones on the surface. Steam was introduced in the 1850s for haulage and later for locomotion. Extensive electrification 1891 from a hydro station on site. Unusually, from 1932 on, an overhead ropeway was used for tipping.

Although using F.R. from the start of operations, direct incline connection was not made until 1854. (Operated until 1964.) From 1879 use was made of the L&NWR exchange siding, and from 1889 the GWR also.

Production is now concentrated in a mill built in the 1950s.

Remains As a working quarry it is not normally possible to view much of the site but there are ruins of mills, drumhouses, inclines etc., including the main exit incline (Inclein Pantrafon) passing under the main road and although lorries provide most of the transport much use is still made of traditional wagons. Prominent is the Inclein Bôn with its big drumhouse, latterly electric powered but once steam driven.

Quarry Tours Ltd provide rail excursions underground including a ride on a powered incline. There is also a fine exhibition centre with a working blacksmith's shop and so on. Many rare examples of artifacts are displayed including a Ceir Gwllt (from Allt Ddu) and examples of the unusual G. Owen, Union Ironworks, Porthmadog, patent saw with chain pulled carriage. The original 1840s office building is near the tour centre and a fine, later, office building is still in use as such.

To the north of the site there are extensive reservoirs and leats, some housing associated with the quarry is in ruins but some is still in use. (16)

LORD Local name for Bowydd or Newborough.

LOWER QUARRY Lowest part of Oakeley = Welsh Slate Co.

LLECHWEDD Y CYD Eastern, early part of Llechwedd.

MAENOFFEREN SH714465

A substantial entirely underground quarry operating on a compact site at over 1300′ amsl. Originally opened in the early 1800s and was unsuccessful until developed by Greaves in the 1850s flourishing during the latter half of the 19th C., and the earlier years of the 20th. Output of 8360 tons with 238 men in 1882, in the '90s grew to over 14,000 tons pa with more than 400 men employed. Two mills, originally water driven contained almost 50 saws and as many trimmers. Locomotive power extensively used. An underground trunk incline was water balanced (later electrified).

Electricity was introduced in the 1890s, a hydro-electric station built in

1918 was still in use in the 1980s. The Greaves company re-acquired the site in the 1970s and using a re-built mill, continued to work it as the last totally underground quarry in the district. In 1980s pioneered the use of wire saws.

Some use was made of the Diffwys incline prior to the construction of the Rhiwbach tramway which ran through the site. Thereafter the No. 1 and 2 inclines of this tramway were used until 1920 when a new incline was made through Votty and Bowydd. After Rhiwbach quarry was acquired in 1928, this incline was abandoned and the Rhiwbach line again used, until 1962. Use was made of the No. 2 incline only, until July 1976, the last working self acting incline in the Industry.

Remains As a working quarry access is restricted. In the late 1980s the mill was still in use served by a network of rail lines. The original brine-bath rheostats control the main underground exit incline. This was 3 tracked, later reduced to 2 tracks.

There are a number of buildings in the mills area and many artifacts. The newer roof slating at the middle of mill shows where the water-wheel was. There is a curious 'kinked flue' to one old engine-house. Adjacent, on the long abandoned David Jones part of the site there is a machine bored adit, relics of an unsuccessful, 1870s, use of a Hunter twin-head boring machine. Of interest is the "cut and cover" tunnel for a line to where tipping was done on the old Votty site. The No. 2 Incline and its remote drumhouse is in excellent condition with machinery virtually complete with trucks and other items near its foot. Alongside is the ruined Votty and Bowydd manager's house. The tramway through Bowydd property to the No. 1 incline is clear and the incline formation itself is intact, It has a compact remote-type drumhouse set into the rock. The No. 3 incline up from the site, leads onto the level main section of the Rhiwbach tramway and has a fine drumhouse. Alongside the first section of this line is the notable, slate lined and slate covered Bowydd leat with its piped extension to feed the Maenofferen power station.

Below the site, is the fine slate floored and guard-railed 'balcony' leading to the partly machine-bored Cooke's level. (22)

MANOD (or old Manod) SH725452

An open working dating from the very early 1800s. It seems to have been worked without buildings or shelter of any kind (at almost 2000′ amsl!) Later incorporated into Graig Ddu workings.

Remains As above not distinguishable from later Graig Ddu work and also much disturbed by untopping.

The old track around Mynydd Manod, by which material went down to the river Dwyryd is traceable. (25)

MANOD SH732455

Also known as New Manod or more properly Bwlch (y Slaters).

Stated to date from early 19th C. but this refers to the old, open workings higher up.

This mainly underground quarry dates from mid 19th C., developing, with a steam powered mill after connection to the Rhiwbach tramway in 1866. In the early 20th C. a subsidiary site was opened at 730458 connected by an incline. Annual tonnages varied considerably but never can have much exceeded 1000. The rock here is more difficult to win than in some nearby quarries requiring more drilling and more powder.

The original route out was via Cwm Teigl, the same route being used after the tramway ceased in the 1930s, modern working having the benefit of a road put in to service the section of the quarry which was used for Art Storage during 1939/45 and by DoE until the early 1980s. Shortly after derequisition serious untopping work commenced.

Remains The site is much disturbed by untopping work and by the cutting of roads, the 1900s incline having been virtually obliterated. The mills area has several interesting buildings including a fine office. The head of the main underground uphaulage incline is to be seen as well as a number of artifacts. The present mill dates from 1985.

The route of the connection to the Rhiwbach tramway, including the reversing loop, is traceable. (26)

MATHEWS Early name for Middle quarry or Gloddfa Ganol.

MOELWYN SH661442

A grandly situated but largely unsuccessful undertaking. Originally opened in the 1820s as small levels on the bleak eastern face of Moelwyn Bach some 1700' amsl. In the 1860s it was developed underground on the southern flank of Moelwyn Mawr, with a mill some distance away at 668444 with 6 saw benches and 7 dressing machines driven by a 40' x 4' wheel fed from Llyn Stwlan. There were 3 barrack buildings.

Active in the 1870s and again in the 1890s, closed about 1900. Material originally removed by packhorse down Cwm Maesgwm by a track built in 1826, but after about 1860 by the F.R. via the spectacular incline system.

Remains At the original workings there are barracks, some other building remains and a possible incline. From the 1860s development, there are adits, some open, but *dangerous* as there are internal shafts. The upper two pitches of the incline system were partly lost when Llyn Stwlan was enlarged in 1960 for the pumped storage scheme. This scheme largely destroyed the mills area but some slight vestiges are to be seen. The 4 pitches down past the generating station to the old FR line, still are a magnificent landscape feature. (2)

MOELWYN BACH Name used for older parts of Moelwyn.

MOELWYN MAWR Name used for newer parts of Moelwyn.

NEWBOROUGH Early name for Bowydd.

NEW WELSH SLATE CO = Cwt y Bugail.

NYTH Y GIGFRAN SH689462
A small and most improbably sited undertaking. Dating from about 1860, adits were driven from a natural ledge in the cliff face. A later adit was driven some 30' below, reached by a rock-cut platform.
Material was lowered by part timber, part stone incline to FR at Glan y Pwll.
After amalgamation with Oakeley, following a lease dispute, there was a tunnel connection to the top of the latter site.
Remains There are two adits open, the upper stopped out to bank, and the lower giving onto a precipitous stone platform. Near the upper adit are some small buildings and some nice rock cut steps, also a possible smithy. The stone part of the incline formation is a prominent feature, and cutting and bolt holes suggest where the wooden extension ran.
Sawn ends suggest sawing on site, in spite of its constriction, and there are verbal accounts of a boiler being lowered from the site in the early 20th C. On the cliff face alongside the site are traces of a Rock Cannon. At Glan y Pwll, alongside the site of the railway siding are some buildings in reuse, possibly connected with the quarry. The tunnel connection with Oakeley is open. (7)

OAKELEY SH695470
An amalgamation of the Upper (Hollands) and Middle quarries (Gloddfa Ganol) in 1878 and the Lower quarry (Welsh Slate) in 1883 and subsequently Cwm Orthin and Nyth y Gigfran made this the largest quarry in the area with an output of almost 60,000 tons pa, and around 1700 men. It was the third largest in the industry, after Penrhyn and Dinorwig. Its early years were troubled by the aftermath of the great collapses of 1882/3, but it eventually comprised workings extending almost from sea level to nearly 1500' on 26 floors (lowest lettered 'R') with a stated 50 miles of rail tracks underground and extensive loco worked surface tramways. There were some 12 mills, the main concentration being at the Middle and Vertical Shaft mills that between them had 53 dressing machines and 53 saw-tables.
About thirty workers cottages stood on the site, and it had its own hospital.
Much use was made of steam power, including, due to constraints of space, the haulage of rubbish. The old open Hollands workings being used for dumping as well as considerable backfilling.
Apart from the surface gravity inclines there were a number of underground uphaulage inclines mainly of the table type. One incline had 6 tracks.

Unusually, a vertical shaft haulage was also used.

When electricity from Cwm Dyli became available in 1906, it gradually replaced steam.

Finished product was lowered directly by incline to the FR. From 1934 the LMSR was also used. There being inclines both from the main site and from the Penybont mill to the railway.

Closed in 1970 but reopened as two separate but associated undertakings, Gloddfa Ganol (with its visitors centre) and Oakeley quarry. Both mainly working untopping. In 1987 a pulverising plant was installed to produce powder for moulded slates.

Remains Owing to tipping, to subsequent work and in part of landscaping, much of the early workings are not to be seen. Some of the Middle quarry area can be visited as part of the Gloddfa Ganol Centre. There are ruins, and reconstructions of mill, dwellings and other buildings, including an electric drumhouse. A number are in reuse. A modern working mill is also in this area.

The Lower quarry area is also being worked with a modern mill but there are many relics still extant, including inclines and tramway formations and a number of buildings.

The Upper quarry which is also part of the Centre has been much altered by more recent work but the topmost part, which was abandoned early is of interest. There are several open workings, accessed by short tunnels, each with its own tramway formation and weigh-house leading to tipping areas. One passes out, through a short tunnel, to a sort of balcony on a clifftop. There is also a powder house and some buildings possibly dating from the original Holland days. There are also vestiges of the upper inclines including one with a unique wooden drum. There is a tunnel through to the Nyth y Gigfran workings, with some chambering off it. At a lower level, there are the remains of the Hollands mill and other workings, a fine rake of lavatories and the long 'Horse level'. There are many artifacts on the ground. Some chambers, are lit and open to the public.

The Penybont (Glan y Don) tip, mill and incline have been removed, but the pillars of the viaduct which gave access over the main-line railway still stand and the incline down to it can be seen. This incline also served as the main route down to the FR, but the old Welsh Slate Co's incline which it replaced has been buried. The two pitch Middle quarry incline is still visible but the old incline which it replaced has long since gone. The zig-zag steps are a prominent feature. (12)

OWAIN GOCH SH704473
Not a quarry but the site of a large water-wheel which, via rods in a 200′ deep shaft, pumped water from levels B and C of Llechwedd to level 2 and also hauled from level B to level 2. (17)

PALMERSTON = Welsh Slate Co.

PANT YR AFON SH697469

Exchange sidings for both Llechwedd and Oakeley. The Llechwedd area has storage sheds and a crane. Also the Llechwedd hydro-electric station, which is still in use. (13)

PANT Y RHYN SH709454

The 1845 mill for Diffwys Casson, subsequently a woollen factory.
Remains Building still in use with disused water-wheel alongside. (20)

PENFFRIDD Early part of Diffwys.

PEN Y BONT = Glan y Don, the detached mills/tip area for Oakeley.

PEN Y FFRIDD = Blaen y Cwm?

PERCIVALS = Bowydd.

RHIW Pre 1818 unsuccessful workings at Welsh Slate Co. site.

RHIWBACH SH740462

About 1812 serious commercial exploitation started on an ancient vernacular site (1760s?) some distance to the south of the later main complex. This site continued in use until the 1880s, the pits probably being hauled and pumped by water-wheel, with possibly some use being made of steam. From the 1860s operations were concentrated at what became the main site. At first by pit working, later underground to the south of the main mill, and afterwards by extensive underground workings on 8 levels to the east.

The substantial mill was steam powered, the same engine winding the big underground incline to the east as well as the exit incline up to the Rhiwbach tramway. Near the mill was a virtual "village" of houses, barracks, a shop and a schoolroom/chapel.

Output 1883, 3187 tons, 130 men

From the 1890s all but the two lowest levels were dewatered by a 600 yard long tunnel that emerged at 745475. This tunnel was also used for some rubble disposal.

Although a large site with an extensive locomotive powered rail network and, of course, its own tramway connection to Blaenau Ffestiniog, tonnages seldom, if ever, exceeded 6000 pa and it was closed several times. Undoubtedly it was subsidised by tramway revenues.

The quarry was electrified in 1934 and finally ceased in 1953. Some men barracked (in a temporary building) until the last days.

Material was originally carried via Cwm Machno for shipment at Trefriw, but from the 1830s until the opening of the Rhiwbach Tramway in the mid 1860s, product was carted to the Afon Dwyryd for shipment. There had been proposals to build a tramway to Penmachno, but in the event the convenience of using the Ffestiniog Railway outweighed the length of track required to reach it, and the Rhiwbach Tramway was built. There may have been thoughts at the turn of the century to use the Cwm Machno route once more via the drainage tunnel, but the tramway continued to be used until closure.

Remains The fine stone-built incline up to the Rhiwbach tramway is a prominent feature, with at its head a massive sheave mounting incorporating a banksman's cabin. Wooden sleepers attached to slate slabs are in place and there are several support wheels for the return rope, some still in their wooden mountings.

At the foot of the incline is the engine house with stack and fuel store alongside. Behind are the ruins of the big mill under the floor of which is a tunnel with slate chutes at intervals. Whilst this seems clearly intended to carry away saw-table waste the method of disposal is unclear.

There are vestiges of a number of other buildings but prominent is a big block that was part dwellings, part barracks. Alongside is a building clearly identifiable as the schoolroom/chapel. Facing these, are traces of the manager's house, unusual in being so close to the workers dwellings and to the operating site. There are carefully decorated lintels etc. incorporated into these buildings and the sweep of road to this domestic site is lined on one side by a most interesting "post & rail" fence entirely of slate. Nearby, over a stream, is a fine rake of lavatories.

At the old site, to the south is a pit with a wheelpit which seems to have hauled and/or pumped it. Further off is an early pit later used as a reservoir, and nearby a possible engine house. There are some traces of several other buildings.

The main underground workings, to the east, begin in a large pit. The ropes to power the incline must have been carried over the mill. This inconvenient arrangement is thought to have arisen as it was originally intended to use a shaft, adjacent to the mill to develop the workings.

The workings may be penetrated by those suitably experienced and equipped, and it is possible to descend 4 levels and emerge through the tunnel (where there is rail track still in place). There is evidence of "pillar robbing" and "cupboarding" and test bores can be seen. There are also a number of bore-cores on the surface, it was unusual to employ test boring in slate quarrying, but it must have been extensively used here. (29)

RHIWBRYFDIR

Early name for Matthews or Middle quarry. Also originally used for the earliest working that became Lower Quarry.

RHYD Y SARN SH690421

Not a quarry but notable as it is believed that before 1802, slate was sawn here in a water powered sawmill. Site of early circular sawing experiments using a horse whim. Possibly the source of the Suwsana Pierce gravestone of 1805 (Llan Ffestiniog) one of the earliest known bearing circular sawmarks.

Remains Wheelpit and leat, present building is a later woollen mill. (8)

SOUTH POLE Local name for Bwlch y Slaters.

TAI'R MURIAU Very early working, lost in later work at Cwm Orthin.

TALYWAENYDD = Westerly part of Llechwedd.

TWLL NEWYDD = Early part of Diffwys.

VOTTY SH706465
Pit working.
Operated from the 1830s to 1870s when it was amalgamated with Bowydd. An early user of saws (1851). Never had any direct rail access, material being brought out via Bowydd. Possibly originally used horse-whim haulage.
Remains Main pit flooded, site much used as a tip area by Maenofferen, so little if any original Votty work can be identified. (18)

WELSH SLATE CO SH693473
This was the original quarry opened by Samuel Holland in 1818, who sold it in 1825 to the Welsh Slate Co. who commenced vigorous and reckless underground working below the two quarries above. There was a complicated transport system including water balanced inclines and a vertical water balance lift. A steam mill, one of the first in the district was built in 1844. Reciprocating sawing having been introduced around 1824. Problems of space later forced tipping to be made on the far side of the railway, which was crossed by a viaduct. A further mill was built on this tip. Connected to FR in 1838 by an incline.
There were serious falls in 1882/3, causing damage to undertakings above, following which legal action resulted in W.E. Oakeley taking over to amalgamate it with the Middle and Upper quarries. In 1882 (immediately prior to the collapse) output was 34234 tons with 720 men employed.
Re-opened on a restricted scale in the 1970s, in late 1980s commenced processing of tips to make raw material for artificial slate.
Remains See Oakeley. (10)

WRYSGAN SH676458
A smallish quarry by Blaenau standards (2078 tons, 96 men) forced to operate on a confined and inaccessible site with limited water supply and beset by geological, financial and legal problems throughout its life. Opened in the 1830s, substantially developed in 1850 with the first mill being built in 1855, with a second mill in 1865, containing a total of 20 saws and 20 dressers. Water power was supplied by the tiny Llyn y

Wrysgan, steam being used later. Access to the underground workings was by 5 adits, one at mills level, two above, served by a balanced incline and two below served by a haulage incline. At the turn of the century output dramatically dropped. Electrified in 1920, it worked intermittently until the late 1940s.

Originally output was lowered part way down the Cwm Orthin side on a balanced incline, taken by pack animal to a landing platform and thence to Tanygrisiau, possibly by sledge.

In 1850 a self-acting incline, possibly the most spectacular in the industry was made to connect direct with the Ffestiniog railway some 600' below. The upper part of the incline being in a tunnel and the approach to the head being by a cutting. As the gradient on the lower section was so slight it was liable to stall. It was relaid as single acting, steam powered but lack of boiler capacity caused delays. In the 1930s it was operated by "borrowing" an electric motor from the mill, and coupling it to the haulage drum each time a journey of empty wagons needed to be raised. In its last days a lorry engine powered the incline.

Alongside the old exit incline a powered incline was built for uphaulage from the lower levels to the mill, it was driven, latterly, by a motor-car engine. Shortly before closure, a rope haulage was used underground.

Remains The obvious feature is the big incline. The access cutting, tunnel and upper part of the formation are in good condition but the lower end has been obliterated by a new road. The old drumhouse has collapsed but much of the drum gear is on site as well as part of the steam haulage engine and the remains of the lorry chassis used as the final power source.

The main mill, like the other buildings, are much degraded, but the interesting tailrace under the mill site can be found, there are only traces of the gravity incline on the Cwm Orthin side but the pack-horse track at its foot, the landing platform (Cei Muliad) and some runs of steps are in good condition. The later, haulage, incline is visible with some parts of its motor-car engine.

The upper incline from the highest adit which is almost 1390' above msl, is in fair condition and at these higher levels are the ruins of some of the early dressing sheds, a small mill and some barracks etc. The stone embanked reservoir, with its double dam, trapping water in a saddle above the site is a nice feature.

Apart from the one at mills level, all adits are open and at the top of the site workings are stoped out to bank. There are relics of the underground rope haulage. The roof is unstable and falls are continuing, so entering is unwise. (5)

SECTION 9: MEIRIONNYDD (NORTH)

North Meirionnydd Section 9

General

This area comprises a large number of small, or very small, quarries which worked isolated Cambrian and Ordivicean outcrops. Some are ancient, many are tiny ephemeral affairs. It includes quarries in the Llan Ffestiniog area but omits some to the east of Bala, which are within the old county boundary, but which geologically and economically form part of the Silurian occurrences of Dinbych. Apart from the former, and the Llanfair quarry which were underground, they are almost entirely open workings, few were mechanised.

Llanfair is open to the public, with a small, but informative, display. There are few artifacts to be seen at the others, but many do offer an interesting insight into small scale working methods, often in remote but scenically rewarding locations.

Transport

Most were far too small to call for any organised system of transport, some carted, and there are several well-constructed access roads to be seen. Some used packhorses and some, doubtless, man-carried.

In the Ffestiniog area Braich Ddu certainly, and others possibly, carted to the Dwyryd (Braich Ddu being the last quarry to do so), and later they may have used the Ffestiniog and Blaenau Railway of 1868 and afterwards the GWR line of 1883.

The 2′g F & BR was almost entirely obliterated by the standard gauge formations. The GWR, which south of Trawsfynydd was closed in 1961, may be readily traced until, after the fine Cwm Prysor viaduct, it was incorporated into the main road. From there it may be followed until its trackbed is drowned in the Trederwyn reservoir.

There is a spectacular stretch of hillside ledge along Cwm Prysor.

In the east, Cletwr used the Llangollen-Dolgellau line after 1868, (closed 1964) and on the coast Llanfair had its own nearby shipping point before the arrival of the Cambrian Railway also in 1868.

1.	SH580288	Llanfair
2.	590266	Coed y Llechau
3.	593252	Pantgwyn
4.	595242	Byrllysg
5.	597243	Brydir
6.	650268	Graig Uchaf
7.	681320	Moel y Gwartheg

8.	681399	Bron Gelli
9.	681408	Cae'n y Coed
10.	684336	Cefn Clawdd
11.	713421	Y Cefn
12.	718384	Braich Ddu
13.	719412	Bron y Rhiw
14.	728318	Gelli Gain
15.	728413	Cwm Cynfal
16.	729414	Bron Goronwy
17.	730445	Chwarel Llew Twrog
18.	731436	Sarn Helen
19.	732317	Bedd Porus
20.	732423	Brynglas
21.	735431	Drum
22.	736446	Cwm Teigl
23.	742444	Y Garnedd
24.	744428	Foelgron
25.	750384	Moel y Croesau
26.	754416	Moel Llechwedd Gwyn
27.	754424	Croes y Ddwy Afon
28.	757304	Tai Cynhaeaf
29.	763388	Conglog
30.	776414	Serw
31.	786396	Chwarel Llechwedd Deiliog
32.	791324	Afon Gain
33.	806376	Cefn Glas
34.	848362	Ffridd y Gloddfa
35.	862291	Ty Mawr
36.	875258	Aran
37.	897330	Coed Cerrig Hwdion
38.	915407	Wernfawr
39.	921371	Tyn y coed
40.	937326	Moelfryn
41.	944338	Buedy'r Ffridd
42.	946341	Gelli Grino
43.	959343	Dolfeurig
44.	975315	Nant y Sarn
45.	985348	Cletwr
46.	988327	Afon Calltwr
47.	995341	Queens
48.	SJ051346	Carnedd y Ci
49.	052336	Cwm Tywyll

ARAN SH875258

Very small open working producing in 1776, later some underground.
Remains Open workings into a steeply dipping exposure. Vestiges of

shelters, lower down 2 adits, the larger one open but flooded. The access track is readily traceable to near quarry. (36)

AFON CALLTWR SH988327 Putative site.
Remains Possible excavation. (46)

AFON GAIN SH791324 Putative site.
Remains Possible excavation. (32)

ALAW MANOD = Cwm Teigl.

BALA LAKE = Ty Mawr.

BEDD PORUS SH732317 Putative site.
Remains Nothing found. (19)

BEUDY'R FFRIDD SH944338
Tiny early working.
Remains Excavation only. (41)

BRAICH DDU SH718384
A shallow, dispersed working that, exploiting the Cambrian series, had a name for producing a good coloured slate.
Material trammed, largely on the level, to a water powered mill where Hunter saws are believed to have been used. Finished product taken to site boundary by tramway for carting to the Afon Dwyryd, for boating, right up to 1868 closure, almost certainly the last quarry to do so. Some small scale extraction into the 1980s, material being lorried to Llechwedd quarry at Blaenau Ffestiniog, for reduction.
Remains The site is somewhat disturbed by later operations, but there are the ruins of a mill with wheelpit, a barracks and some other buildings, including a possible earlier mill. A notable feature is the rough slab causeway, with an interesting bridge that carried the tramway to a loading point on the road. (12)

BRON GELLI SH681399
Unlikely to be slate.
Remains Possible excavation. (8)

BRON GORONWY SH729414
Underground working producing slab and roofing slab on a small scale.
Remains Ruins of a tiny mill possibly housing a hand powered circular saw, vestiges of a forge. Tip and access track partly encroached on by forestry road widening.
Underground, a tunnel, partly worked out to bank, leads to chambering. Later downward working in this tunnel left inner workings isolated. (16)

BRON Y RHIW SH719412 (or Bron Erw)
Small underground working with 2 tandem adits, possibly never had any buildings.
Remains Collapsed adits. (13)

BRYNGLAS SH732423
Underground working on a small scale, in small interconnecting chambers reducing in an adjacent mill. Later, working was commenced from the other side of the hill and an incline built, but this work seems to have been confined to some extraction from a short, unfinished tunnel. Closed 1920s.
Remains Southern adit, seems to have been started, then continued at a lower level. There are the remains of the incline drumhouse and the tramway round to the mill at the northern adit, this drumhouse and some other buildings are in fair condition, but although there is water available, it does not appear to have been used for power. There is a well engineered track leading to the Ffestiniog road that may have been intended as a tramway but there is no evidence that rail was ever laid.
There is some interesting and readily accessible chambering, with snatch-blocks and wires suggesting a portable haulage from the latter small-scale days. The southern tunnel comes to blind end with only working near the entrance. There are remains of an 'A' frame. (20)

BRYDIR SH597243
Small underground working.
Remains Run-in adit. (5)

BYRLLYSG SH595242
Putative site.
Remains Ground disturbance. (4)

CAE'N Y COED SH681408
Small working in a river gorge, possibly before 1754. Material taken by tramway to a water powered mill which is believed to have had a Hunter saw. Probably the first user of boats on the Dwyryd and a possible source of a very early hand-sawn gravestone at Llan Ffestiniog (William Davies 1775).
Remains Launder pillars in quarrying area, tramway formation and incline (much degraded) to near mill building, with wheelpit. Mill subsequently used as woollen mill. Farm on site named Ffatri. (9)

CARNEDD Y CI SJ051346
Tiny hillside scratching.
Remains Slight traces of excavation. (48)

CEFN BODLOSGAD = Y Cefn.

CEFN CLAWDD SH684336
A small pit working accessed by an adit that also drained it, hand worked.
Remains Pit and adit, rubbish run and possible working area to south of the road. No buildings. (10)

CEFN GLAS SH806376
Putative site.
Remains Some digging in forestry. (33)

CHWAREL BRYN LLECH = Bron Goronwy.

CHWAREL LLECHWEDD DEILIOG SH786396
Tiny roadside working.
Remains Virtually none. (31)

CHWAREL LLEW TWROG SH730445
Small underground working.
Remains Tiny dressing shelter, using a rock outcrop as a third wall. The underground tunnel is surprisingly long for so little rubbish at the surface. Tunnel about 150 yards long ends in 2 branches with some limited roofing shafts cut. There is some bar rail in situ, set directly into tenoned sleepers. (17)

CHWAREL OWEN SION = Bron Goronwy.

CLETWR SH985348
Open quarry developed into a deep pit working (possibly with underground workings off it?) with a tunnel connecting to a mill lower down the hillside. Finished product taken by cartway to the main line railway. 1882 output 50 tons 6 men. Stated to have had a 12hp steam engine and 10 saws.
Remains Site now largely in forestry. At edge of the pit is a ruin of a small building and nearby another in reuse as a shooting lodge, both presumably dating from the early open workings. The mills have been levelled but vestiges of a wheelpit and underfloor water channels are to be seen. The access tunnel is blocked (dammed as a water source). The cartway is partly traceable, a stopped up arch shows where it passed under the main road near the railway. (45)

COED CERRIG HWDION SH897330
Putative site.
Remains Possible excavation. (37)

COED Y LLECHAU SH590266
Hillside quarry on two levels with incline down to mill.
Remains Site much disturbed by later stone quarrying. There is a fine mill

building with a nice graduated slate roof and other buildings in reuse. The incline has been quarried away. (2)

CONGLOG SH763388
Putative site of slate working.
Remains Suggest stone working only. Site was a source of material for the construction of Cwm Prysor viaduct. The temporary tramway for this purpose is traceable. (29)

CROES Y DDWY AFON SH754424
Underground, worked sporadically on a small scale from around 1870 to the 1920s, material hauled out by incline to a water powered mill. Finished product removed by cart. Re-opened 1987 (as open pit) by workers displaced following the Blaenau Ffestiniog strike. Thus repeating 19th C. happenings in the Ogwen valley and elsewhere. Later vigorously untopped.
Remains Apart from the fine dam and a leat system, little of the original surface structures are extant. New buildings being erected in the late 1980s. Virtually all of the compact underground workings, on two levels, have been destroyed by modern untopping work. (27)

CWM CYNFAL SH728413
Small underground trial, possibly metal, not slate.
Remains Adit and small building. Tunnel goes in about 30 yards and turns left and right to blind ends. (15)

CWM TEIGL SH736446
Underground. In spite of its trifling scale it had a water powered mill, material carted to Ffestiniog.
Remains Small mill which probably contained one saw-table. Wheelpit, launder pillars and a neat slate lined leat leading down from a small reservoir on hill above. At a nearby trial is an interesting vaulted half-underground shelter. Adit collapsed, access track readily traceable. (23)

CWM TYWYLL SJ052336
Pit, very early, 1706? Possibly some underground, quite large for an entirely unmechanised site.
Remains Water-filled pit, dressing shed, wall with curious cwtch, rubbish runs, stock of slates, (10x16 and 8x14). Water on site but no evidence that it was used for power. (49)

DOLFEURIG SH959343
Putative site, may not have been slate.
Remains Excavation. (43)

DRUM SH735431

Pit/underground, sporadically worked from 1860s, originally a hillside working with hand dressing, but deepened into pits and developed underground. Around 20 men employed producing about 500 tons pa. Material carted to main road.

Remains At upper level, dressing sheds etc. and a building that housed the haulage winch. Ruined drumhouse at head of the well engineered incline. Mill building. From one pit an incline descends underground into water, but chambers are accessible from the southern pit. Some distance away are 3 collapsed adits with tramway formations, tips and weigh-houses and on one level a curious building. The original access track to the site is traceable and the track to the mill is well defined, it appears to have been levelled as a tramway but there is no evidence that rails were ever laid. (21)

FOELGRON SH744428

Open quarry, opened around 1850, later some underground. No water was available at the quarry, so when a water-powered mill was erected it was sited at SH747423, alongside the main road and connected to the working by a tramway. 112 tons, 4 men 1883.

Remains Owing to subsequent granite working little to be seen directly connected to the slate operation. There is a fine 5 bayed building which may have originally been for the slate operation. The tramway is defined by the present approach road. The mill, originally breast wheel driven, later oil engined, was destroyed in the 1980s during landscaping work. (24)

FFRIDD Y GLODDFA SH848362

Tiny open working.
Remains Excavation and ground disturbance. (34)

GELLI GAIN SH728318 Putative site.
Remains Possible excavation. (14)

GELLI GRINO SH946341

Tiny open working.
Remains Excavation only. (42)

GLANLLYN May be Tŷ Mawr.

GRAIG UCHAF SH650268

Tiny open pit working.
Remains Excavation. (6)

HENDRE DDU = Braich Ddu.

LLANFAIR SH580288

A moderate sized, almost totally underground working opened around the 1860s. It exploited an excellent band of Cambrian series rock, going down five levels. It was the only quarry to work this particular occurrence owing to the cost penalty of underground working from above and closed after only a few years. Re-opened at the turn of the century it closed again during WW1. Between the wars machinery was installed for the crushing of stone and for the production of tiles, about 20 men being employed. Used as an explosive store in WW2 it was opened as a visitor centre in the 1960s.

Product was loaded onto the Cambrian Railway, (to whom they may have supplied ballast) but earlier had been shipped from Pensarn wharf on the Afon Artro, little use being made of their product in the locality.

Remains Several chambers are open to the public and some of the buildings have been reused in this connection. The tramway may be traced and there are some buildings at the nearby Pensarn wharf. (1)

LLECHRWD = Cae'n Coed.

LLYN EINION = Pant Gwyn.

MIGNEINT Possibly early workings, Serw?

MOELFRYN SH937326
Small pit working.
Remains Lost in forestry. (40)

MOEL LLECHWEDD GWYN SH754416
Possible trial.
Remains Almost nothing. (26)

MOEL Y CROESAU SH750384
Tiny open pit.
Remains Only the pit. (25)

MOEL Y GWARTHEG SH681320
Small underground working, entirely unmechanised.
Remains Two collapsed adits and a dressing area. There is a tiny dug out stone lined shelter with storage niches, which was possibly the sole shelter on this bleak, remote site. It is unlikely that any wheeled cart could have reached this site, there is no trace of even an access path. It is possible that slate was taken away on the backs of the men who produced it. (7)

NANT DERBYNIAD = Serw.

NANT Y PISTYLL GWYN = Moel Llechwedd Gwyn.

NANT Y SARN SH975315
Putative site. Working 1880s?
Remains Lost in forestry. (44)

PANTGWYN SH593252
Small underground working.
Remains Flooded tunnel, and collapsed workings, rubbish runs, possible
building traces. Adjacent other tunnelling, (metal trials?). (3)

PEN Y LLYN Alternative name for Foel Gron?

QUEENS SH995341
Small open working, with possibly some underground.
Remains Ruined buildings, wheelpit, flooded pit. Site much disturbed by
forestry. (47)

SARN HELEN SH731436
Underground, trial only?
Remains Adit leading to a small flooded chamber. (18)

SERW SH776414
A small pit working, probably entirely unmechanised, material carted to
the Ffestiniog-Bala road by a trackway.
Remains Two small dressing sheds, one of which has a neat little storage
alcove. Another structure appears to be a dwelling, but has no trace of a
fireplace, also some abutments for a possible haulage. The access road
though well engineered in places, has largely vanished into boggy ground.
(30)

TAI CYNHAEAF SH757304
Small pit, vernacular use only.
Remains Pit only. (28)

TYDDYN LLYWARCH This may be Tŷ Mawr.

TŶ MAWR SH862291
Pit working.
Remains Used as rubbish dump and landscaped. (35)

TYN Y COED SH921371
Tiny pit.
Remains Almost nothing. (39)

WERNFAWR SH915407
Tiny pit working.
Remains Almost nil. (38)

Y CEFN SH713421
Series of shallow pit workings, of very early date.
Remains Site now occupied by golf course. (11)

Y GARNEDD SH742444
Tiny underground working.
Remains Collapsed adit, no buildings. Waste suggests some production.
(23)

Mawddach Area Section 10

General

This area comprises a number of quarries dispersed around the valley of the lower Mawddach, seeking to exploit occurrences, mainly of the Cambrian series.

Most were small, some were very small, but some of the less remote ones were of respectable size.

Some were handily sited but others, such as Gloddfa Gwanas were most improbably located.

Arthog, Henddol, Penrhyngwyn and a few others have substantial remains, the latter two include underground workings of some extent. Most of the rest were open workings, with few remains, but all offer some insight into working methods and several offer the bonus of a spectacular view.

Transport

Quarries in this area almost exclusively carted to shipping points. In the case of Cefn Gam this involved the building of a considerable length of road, most of which survives. Gloddfa Gwanas used public roads, but to reach them an ambitious zig-zag cart track, still traceable, was built.

Henddol/Golwern had an incline system which after 1868 enabled them to benefit from a short, level, cartage to the Cambrian Railway, and so develop.

Arthog, was the only quarry to have direct tramway connection to the railway, but closed within a year of becoming so linked.

1.	SH603191	Ffridd Olchfa
2.	605205	Egryn
3.	605206	Hendre Eirian
4.	619122	Henddol
5.	621122	Golwern
6.	621127	Friog
7.	623133	Bwlch Gwyn
8.	625129	Bryn Neuadd
9.	625131	Bryn Gwyn
10.	626092	Peniarth
11.	630135	Tyddyn Shieffre
12.	631125	Cyfannedd
13.	649148	Tyn y Coed
14.	652152	Arthog

SECTION 10: MAWDDACH

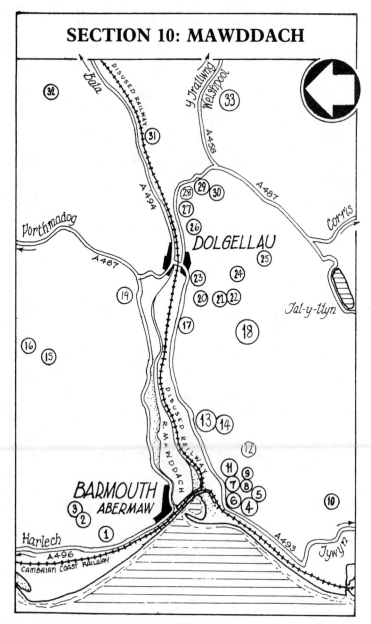

15.	678245	Cwm Mynach
16.	680256	Cefn Gam
17.	702184	Ffridd Isaf
18.	704149	Penrhyngwyn
19.	709198	Ty Nant
20.	717171	Rhiw Rhedyn Cochion
21.	718161	Tan y Gader
22.	720161	Bryn Rhug
23.	724176	Clogwyn
24.	728160	Bryn Mawr
25.	732152	Pant yr Onnen
26.	741175	Fron Serth
27.	748178	Groes Lwyd
28.	749181	Coed Dolgun Uchaf
29.	755175	Coed Ffridd Arw
30.	756174	Pant Cra
31.	777195	Garth
32.	784233	Cae'r Defaid
33.	798160	Gloddfa Gwanas

ARTHOG SH652152

Terraced hillside quarry opened in mid 18th C., operating on several levels connected by inclines. The lowest level was developed into a pit, accessed by a short tunnel. Originally hand dressing on terraces, but later a tramway took material across the main road, possibly to a mill, and through a short tunnel to a trackway down to a small jetty. This was replaced by an incline and tramway, later extended to a railway siding. In 1868, a substantial mill, probably for sawing only, was built. Closed the following year.

Remains On the terraces there are some much decayed vestiges of dressing sheds, drumhouses, weigh-houses etc. The tramway that was built to utilise Tyn y Coed quarry for rubbish dumping is a prominent feature. At ground level recent bulk working has destroyed the area near the foot of incline but the exceptionally fine dry stone tramroad embankment to the mill is extant. A smithy, possibly a pre-existing house, stands. The mill area is now a caravan park, the (dated) mill is in nice condition, the short tunnel is open. The stone incline formation down to the railway is in excellent condition. (14)

BRYN GWYN SH625131

Small hillside working, several trial levels.
Remains Excavations, some traces of buildings. (9)

BRYN MAWR SH728160

Putative site.
Remains Possible ground disturbance. (24)

BRYN NEUADD SH625129
A tiny pit working, operated around 1860.
Remains Excavation. (8)

BRYN RHUG SH720161
Putative site.
Remains Possible ground disturbance. (22)

BWLCH GWYN SH623133
Small underground working, active around 1867.
Remains Collapsed adit. (7)

CAE'R DEFAID SH784233
An underground working from which vast amounts of country rock but little slate seem to have emerged although in 1897 it was offered for sale as having 'great potential'.
Remains Two adits, the upper one chambered out to bank shows little sign of profitable activity, the lower one which leads to some limited chambering, does seem to have produced some slate. There are some ruins of a small building, some very limited tramway formations and a short access track to the road. (32)

CEFN GAM SH680256
A series of shallow pits worked successively over a long period. The slate was of a good colour, but although it did not readily split, where it did, it made a tough flexible product.
Initially everything was hand-dressed, at some time a water powered mill was installed and later, water powered haulage. An attempt was made to avoid haulage by accessing the workings via a tunnel, but this project was not completed. Finally there was some very small scale hand re-working on the site. Finished product was taken down to the river by a well engineered road.
Remains A number of buildings on site including dressing sheds, a workshop/office and a mill with launder pillars adjacent. The alignment of a slot in the mill structure suggests that the mill power was used, or proposed to be used, for haulage out of the pit. To the south is the exit of the tunnel from the pit and remains suggesting that some slate was taken out this way and the possible intention to re-site the mill at this point.
In the pit are the shelters used in the final small scale operations.
There is a further building, possibly a barracks and a fine manager's house. This latter has a nice underground food store and the garden still shows evidence of careful cultivation.
Except near the quarry itself the access road is in good condition, the lower section subsequently serving the Diffwys metal mine. (16)

CLOGWYN SH724176
Almost certainly not slate.
Remains Excavation only. (23)

COED DOLGUN UCHAF SH749181
Putative site.
Remains In forestry. (28)

COED FFRIDD ARW SH755175
Almost certainly not slate.
Remains Excavation only. (29)

CROWN = Penrhyngwyn.

CWM MYNACH SH678245
Very small pit working alongside track to Cefn Gam.
Remains Small quarry face. (15)

CYFANNEDD SH631125
Underground. Was, from around the 1840s, a metal mine, slate was found
and worked 1870/80.
Remains Possible cobbing floor re-used for slate dressing. Stock of small
slates. Lower down hill crusher house and other metal-mining remains.
Adit is open and underground is a slate block awaiting haulage. (12)

EGRYN SH605205
Small hillside quarry, material carted to road at Egryn Abbey.
Remains Two small buildings and possible powder house. (2)

FFRIDD ISAF SH702184
Putative site.
Remains In forestry. (17)

FFRIDD OLCHFA SH603191
Very small hillside quarry.
Remains Excavation. (1)

FRIOG SH621127
Ancient site?
Remains Possible signs of quarrying. (6)

FRON SERTH SH741175
Putative site.
Remains Excavation only. (26)

GARTH SH777195
Possible trial.
Remains In forestry. (31)

GLODDFA GWANAS SH798160
Small workings, producing a poorish slate, remotely situated on either side of a 2000 ft peak, probably sporadically worked over several periods. Initial development was to the west of the summit, with subsequent working from the east. Seems to have produced slab as well as roofing slate. Sawing done on a hand powered circular saw.

Material taken away by a short incline to a most elaborately engineered cart road, which was later extended right to the quarry. This road seems to have been preceded by one or possibly two, pack-animal tracks.

Remains To the west a tiny sawmill, an office/forge and a dwelling, the incline formation, partly tipped over, and a collapsed tunnel to the pit working. To the north a small barracks. To the east, at a lower level some dressing shelters and a collapsed tunnel to the working. This tunnel has itself been worked for product. The two tunnels are the only places where there is any sign of (hand) drilling, so one assumes that explosives were not used for quarrying. Other than on the incline, there is no evidence of any rail ever having been laid. The road is a spectacular feature. (33)

GOLWERN SH621122
A pit working, opened in 1865 it was never successful with a limited output (50 tons 4 men 1882) but its somewhat elaborate incline arrangements provided a route down to the road for the neighbouring Henddol quarry. Material was carted to the railway, the opening of which provided a spur to quarrying in this area. Closed in 1915.

Originally worked as a hillside quarry with hand dressing, with an incline system to the road. Later it was developed as a pit, accessed by tunnels. The lowest tunnel was blocked to provide a water source for a mill at road level, possibly never completed, to reduce Henddol material.

Remains On the highest, earliest level are dressing sheds and a welgh-house with the wagon platform still in situ. There is a nice flight of steps down to the next level which seems to have been built on a disused incline. At this level are further buildings and a notable underfloor horizontal sheave, still in place, and three little tunnels which carried, respectively, the two ropes and the brake rod, thus enabling a rubbish run track to pass between the sheave and the incline crimp. Nearby there is a stone slab covered culvert of unknown purpose.

On the next level down is a further rake of dressing sheds and a tunnel which divides to enter the pit at two points. The pit is partly flooded making an attractive blue lagoon. On this level is some unusual light gauge track and the remains of at least three De Winton trimming shears and of a saw-table. From this level, the long incline goes down to the road. The drumhouse has collapsed but the fragments of the drum are on site, lying in a wheelpit that possibly was never used. There is a further working level below this with a rake of dressing sheds, presumably where the lowest, now blocked, adit emerged. Also there is road access to this level. There are at least three fine stone archways on this site.

At road level, there are some remnants of the mill. (5)

GROES LWYD SH748178
Possible tiny digging, trial only?
Remains In forestry. (27)

HENDDOL SH619122
Underground, with some hillside working, commenced in 1865, it was rather more successful (410 tons 40 men 1883), than the neighbouring Golwern with which it was run in conjunction. After the latter closed in 1915 the Golwern incline and mill continued to be used until final closure in 1928. Although annual tonnages cannot have exceeded a few hundred, it employed, together with Golwern, up to 80 men.

Remains At the higher levels are 2 nice weigh-houses, with fireplaces, for which the steeply sloping ground provides deep mechanism pits. On the next level down is a most crude miniature drum for a primitive incline to the level below, possibly from late, small-scale work. There are a number of dressing sheds and some well constructed buildings. From the lowest level a tunnel (open) provides access and drainage for the workings, some chambering may be entered, various rails are situ, including Hughes bar rail. An intermediate level (2 floors up), gated, leads to some chambering. The highest level appears to have been a trial only. There is an air shaft. The lowest incline seems to have originally gone right down to road level but later appears to have joined the Golwern incline presumably with some interchange arrangement. (4)

HENDRE EIRIAN SH605206
Small, entirely unmechanised pit working producing a green slate. Material removed by a cart track.
Remains Tunnel to pit, some traces of small buildings. (3)

PANT CRA SH756174
Possible site.
Remains Some excavation. (30)

PANT YR ONNEN SH732152
Very small, possibly not slate?
Remains Excavation only. (25)

PENIARTH SH626092
Also at 625089 and 624084, virtually tiny scratchings with the possibility of carting down the Dysynni valley by existing roads.

Remains Excavations and rubbish with a trace of one small building near main site. (10)

PENRHYNGWYN SH704149

Open/Underground. Originally a small, unmechanised open quarry, later developed on several levels underground, probably at different times. There was some sawing on site, a mill was built but possibly never completed. Such material as was produced was carted down to the nearby road. Output 250 tons 47 men 1883.

Remains Topmost level, old open working. Next level down, old working deepened into a pit with incline giving access from a lower level possibly was a waterwound uphaulage. Rubbish runs, two buildings with fireplaces and trackway downhill.

Third level down, collapsed adit, forge and other buildings including barracks and a drumhouse and, some distance off, a powder house.

Fourth level down, rake of dressing sheds, weigh-house and alongside the river, a well embanked tramway, partly collapsed, to an adit (run in).

Lowest working level, possible weigh-house, a further rake of dressing sheds and a tramway to an adit with recent metal arching and door, which leads to some chambering.

At foot of incline a largish mill type building possibly never completed, formed by twice extending a pre-existing structure. There is very little mill-waste but there are some circular-sawn ends around so power sawing was presumably done. Near, but not directly adjacent to, and at right angles on a lower level, is a wheelpit (40' x 2'?). It is not clear what this drove or how. It seems older than, at least the extension, of the 'mill' building. The leat for this wheel is clearly seen. There is one other office type building on this level, another structure may have been a barracks. There are big tonnages of bad rock all over the site. (18)

PLAS CANOL Alternative name for Ffridd Olchfa.

RHIW RHEDYN COCHION SH717171
Not slate?
Remains Excavation only. (20)

RHOBELL Possibly = Cae'r Defaid.

TAN Y GADER SH718161
Putative site.
Remains Possible excavation. (21)

TYDDYN GARRET = Coed Ffridd Arw.

TYDDYN SHIEFFRE SH630135
A series of shallow open workings on the eastern slope, connected to

others on the western side, by a tunnel. Short incline from tunnel to a mills area. Material carted to the railway. Opened in 1865, closed 1900. *Remains* Mills area largely cleared but near the tunnel entrance are some buildings in agricultural reuse and the house of the quarry name is still in occupation. The tunnel is blocked. (11)

TY NANT SH709198
Tiny open quarry.
Remains Excavation only. (19)

TYN Y COED SH649148
A small, early working, later used as a dump for Arthog waste.
Remains Very little as so much material has been dumped in the old pits. Notable however is a drystone tunnel some 50 yards long, built to prevent the Arthog material blocking an occupation road. (13)

TY UCHA Probably Cae'r Defaid.

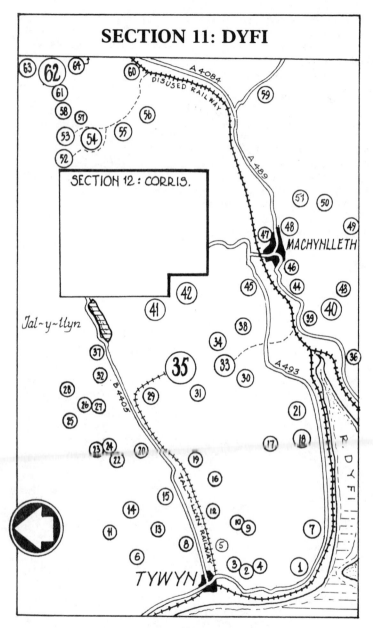

Dyfi Area Section 11

General

This area comprises those quarries in and around the Dyfi Valley (other than the Corris area — Section 12).

Although most of the quarries were small, there were several important ones such as Bryn Eglwys and Minllyn and some others such as Hendre Ddu, Maes y Gamfa, Fron Goch and Alltgoch, which have worthwhile remains. There are also some remote, but fascinating sites such as Darren.

Apart from the small scratchings, quarrying was mostly underground.

Transport

The area is of interest for its diversity of transport routes. Almost all the quarries were too small to support, or to require elaborate arrangements. Long cartages were frequently involved, mainly to Aberdyfi, which for a time had a regular export trade.

Two quarries had their own tramway links to a wharves on the river, the short Fron Goch line and the much longer Cwm Ebol tramway.

Famous, is the Talyllyn Railway of 1866, serving Bryneglwys quarry, the first quarry-to-the-sea route designed and built as a narrow gauge steam railway.

Curious, is the little Hendre Ddu 2'g line, serving several quarries in and near the Angell valley. Originally horse-drawn, it had a variety of lash-up locos before its late 1930s closure. Much of the main line of it now forms the valley road and most of the branches are readily traceable.

It loaded onto the Mawddwy Railway, at Aberangell, which ran from a junction with the Cambrian line at Cemaes Road to Dinas Mawddwy, it opened in 1867 to serve Minllyn and other quarries. The sole private Standard Gauge railway primarily built as a slate quarry route. Closed in 1951 the trackbed is readily traceable.

1.	SN600962	Yr Horon
2.	600998	Fronheulog
3.	SH603005	Ty Mawr
4.	SN604994	Caethle
5.	SH614010	Cwm Cynfal
6.	614073	Cwm Ych
7.	SN620964	Alltgoch
8.	SH621040	Ffridd Cocyn
9.	623013	Braich y Rhiw
10.	625017	Rhyd yr Onnen

11.	625091	Afon Dyffryn
12.	630029	Pandy
13.	630055	Perfeddnuant
14.	634070	Garth Fach
15.	643048	Nant y Mynach
16.	645030	Ffridd Llwyn Hynydd
17.	SN650998	Dys y Nant
18.	652972	Pant Eidal
19.	SH653043	Dolgoch
20.	664062	Tai Newyddion
21.	SN664972	Fron Goch
22.	SH666084	Castell y Bere
23.	669094	Gernos
24.	670087	Llechwedd
25.	671097	Pennant
26.	675095	Tyn y Fach
27.	676091 etc.	Cerrig y Felin
28.	678098	Gwastad Fryn
29.	679055 etc.	Foel Fawr
30.	682012	Rhaeadr
31.	682053	Hendre
32.	685088	Nant yr Eira
33.	689017	Cwm Ebol
34.	693024	Afon Alice
35.	695054	Bryn Eglwys
36.	SN698961	Glandyfi
37.	SH700089	Maes y Pandy
38.	706014	Pen y Bryn
39.	SN715991	Morben
40.	717977	Llyn Fant
41.	SH719071	Glyniago
42.	723057	Darren
43.	SN724976	Coed Cefn Maes Mawr
44.	SH732000	Nawllyn
45.	735015	Nant yr Eryr
46.	SH737002	Craig yr Ogof
47.	749014	Gallt y Gog
48.	755005	Parc
49.	SN755963	Cwm Rhaeadr
50.	763992	Coed Pant Bach
51.	SH763000	Pont Faen
52.	799125	Hendre Ddu
53.	818127	Maes y Gamfa
54.	822117	Gartheiniog
55.	828107	Esgair Angell
56.	830095	Coed y Chwarel

57.	831125	Tal y Mieryn
58.	836138	Bwlch Siglen
59.	844031	Wynnstay Castle
60.	845102	Clipiau
61.	846136	Cae Abaty
62.	852139	Minllyn
63.	855148	Targwrmoel
64.	872134	Pen y Graig

AFON ALICE SH693024
Putative site.
Remains Lost in forestry. (34)

AFON DYFFRYN SH625091
Possibly could have been slate trial.
Remains Excavation only. (11)

ALLTGOCH SN620964
Underground, a small working operating for a few years until 1882.
Material carted to Aberdyfi.
Remains Much of site wooded or disturbed, a C.G.I. building occupies the presumed mill site. The main adit leads to some chambering. Another adit some 70′ lower leads to a shaft down from main adit, there is an upper adit but this seems to be lost in forestry. (7)

BRAICH Y RHIW SH623013
Small hillside quarry on two levels, material may have been carted to Talyllyn Railway.
Remains Excavation only. (9)

BRYNEGLWYS SH695054
The largest and most important quarry in the area.
Early 19th C. surface workings developed, underground, in the 1860s by Lancashire men said to be diversifying due to a shortage of cotton during the American Civil War. Considerable developments were made including use of water power for hauling and compressed air, as well as for driving the several mills. There was a writing slate factory. There was an extensive network of tramways and inclines. During the latter part of the last century output exceeded 8000 tons pa and over 250 were employed. (1883 7996 tons 282 men) Final closure in 1947.
Prior to the opening of the Talyllyn Railway, material was packhorsed to Pennal.
Remains Most of the buildings were demolished in the early 1980s, but much is traceable on the surface. The underground workings may be entered but parts are most unsafe.
The first workings seen on approaching by the quarry road are the old

Broad vein workings and the tramway formation to the top of the Beudynewydd incline down to the Lower mill area. Below the road is an adit serving those workings which were connected by a tramway to a point part way down that incline. Just beyond where the access road crosses the Llaeron stream are, on the left the remnants of the compressor/generator house and drumhouse for the water-wheel winding gear which wound from an adit some distance uphill. Associated with this is a very fine slate lined leat and launder pillars. Behind are incline formations down from the upper or narrow vein workings and one having a drumhouse still standing. To the right, are the ruins of the manager's house and other buildings.

Further on, near the main adit, were the old and new mills, workshops, smithy, magazine etc. and a two storey barracks, and further inclines down from the upper workings. Behind the rubbish tips above the main adit is the most notable item on site, the elaborate double wheel housing that hauled up the main chain incline from the narrow vein workings. Besides the wheel pits and drum housings there are rope tunnels and several maintenance and access passages.

High above the quarry site are remains of the reservoirs and their leat systems.

In the Lower mill area at the foot of the Beudynewydd incline is the extensive level area of the storage yard and here are the ruins of the big, turbine powered mill and some other minor buildings.

The tramway formation is readily traceable past the Cantrybedd cottages to the head of Cantrybedd incline. The drumhouse being set well back from the crimp, the brake was controlled by a long rod. The incline may be followed, with some difficulty, and via a spectacular formation, high above the river, to the Alltwyllt incline which made end on connection to the Talyllyn Railway and is now incorporated into a designated walk.

The Village incline on the Talyllyn Railway mid-way between Nant Gwernol station and Abergynolwyn station, which took general supplies down to the village, is traceable. (35)

BWLCH SIGLEN SH836138

This is the site of the Red Dragon "Gold" mine, but slate is reputed to have been worked here or nearby.

Remains Nothing slate connected found. (58)

CAE ABATY SH846136

A small pit working, with material being uphauled, latterly at least, by a derrick and taken by a short self-acting incline to a dressing area.

Originally material was carted down Nant Blaen y Cwm but later hauled up a shoulder of Foel Dinas to a tramway connecting to Minllyn quarry.

Remains There are several buildings on site but no evidence of water power. There are some artifacts including derrick remains and incline drum. The tramway to Minllyn seems to have been light track laid directly on the ground, leaving little trace. At the haulage point 848137 there are vestiges of a building some machine parts, but no hint of power source. (61)

CAETHLE SN604994
A small open working, material carted to Tywyn.
Remains Almost none. Site now caravan park. (4)

CARDIGAN SLATE WORKS = Glandyfi.

CARLYLE = Dinas Mawddwy = Minllyn.

CASTELL Y BERE SH666084
Putative trial.
Remains Possible slight working. (22)

CERRIG Y FELIN SH676091 and 678094
Possible trial.
Remains Some surface disturbance. (27)

COED CEFN MAES MAWR SN724976
Putative site.
Remains In forestry? (43)

COED PANT BACH SN763992
Possible trials.
Remains Run-in adit? In forestry. (50)

COED RHONWYDD = Pen y Bryn.

COED Y CHWAREL SH830095
A small open quarry, slab, probably closed end of 19th C. Used Hendre Ddu tramway.
Remains Site lost in forestry. (56)

COED Y FFRIDD = Gartheiniog.

CLIPIAU SH845102
Trial?
Remains Possible ground disturbance. (60)

CRAIG YR OGOF SH737002
Possibly slate.
Remains Excavation only. (46)

CWM CYNFAL SH614010
Tiny open quarry little if any, useful make produced.
Remains Only the pit itself. (5)

CWM EBOL SH689017
Open pits, which clearly failed to provide a return on the capital expended. Output in 1883 260 tons 9 men.
Originally several pit workings were connected by an incline to a dressing area. Later a water powered mill and a new, substantial stone incline were built. This latter incline was later replaced by a tramway and a third, shorter incline. Originally product removed by cart, later a tramway took material to a shipping point on the Dyfi.
Remains A substantial mill and other buildings, incline formations etc. The "new" incline has slate sleepers and remnants of bridge rail. Above the site is a reservoir, now dry and the ruins of a pre-existing farm building that must have been under water.
The most notable feature is the easily traceable tramway to the river at 702996. There is the formation of an incline at 695009. Near this incline is a small quartz mine and spillage shows that the tramway was also used to carry this product to the main road near Pennal. (33)

CWMERAU Alternative name for Glandyfi.

CWM RHAEADR SN755963
Very small, operated around 1880s/1890s, possibly for local use only.
Remains Almost nothing, site disturbed by forestry road. (49)

CWM YCH SH614073 Possible trial.
Remains Traces of ground disturbance. (6)

CYLLELLOG Probably a name given by Cae Graig Slate Co., to Pen y Bryn.

DARREN SH723057
Pit/underground working that was a vain attempt to develop an ancient site, which, located on a packhorse route had provided a handy source for local use over very many years.
In the 1850s a first attempt was made to work the slate underground and a mill and other buildings were erected. The iron content made the slate difficult to sell and work was abandoned. A further attempt was made at lower level in the hope that a better product would result but this was unsuccessful. Subsequently there was some small scale working on the opposite side of the hill, but quality apart, the lack of water for power and the near impossibility of transport made this site a very doubtful proposition.

Remains Near the collapsed adit which passed under the ancient quarry, are a number of buildings including a tiny mill which contains fragments of a hand operated saw-table. There is a big stockyard area and this, and a large area of the adjacent ground is covered with many thousands of finished slates, most are broken or decayed but at least 10,000 remain intact. At the lower adit is another small mill with remnants of machinery. Lack of waste suggests that little work was done here.

Around the southern shoulder of the hill are several collapsed adits and a small dressing shed. There is some finished product on the ground, of rather better quality than that near the main working.

Unusually, for such a remote site, there are no barracks or other dwellings. (42)

DINAS MAWDDWY = Minllyn.

DOLGOCH SH653043
A small operation, that nevertheless merited its own siding on the Talyllyn Railway.
Remains Virtually none, run-in adit. (19)

DYS Y NANT SN650998
Extremely small underground operation worked in the 1850s, material carted to the road at 668998.
Remains Spoil only, adits collapsed. (17)

ESGAIR ANGELL SH828107
Site of at least a trial.
Remains Lost in forestry. (55)

FOEL FAWR SH679055 & 681057
Putative trials.
Remains Lost in forestry. (29)

FFRIDD COCYN SH621040
Possibly slate.
Remains Excavation only. (8)

FFRIDD LLWYN HYNYDD SH645030
Very small, possibly never produced.
Remains Excavation only. (16)

FRON GOCH SN664972
Underground. Although a small operation it had a steam powered mill and its own shipping jetty. Originally an open working with a track to the beach, but since this route was cut by the 1866/67 railway construction, one assumes that it was underground by this time. Much money was spent

during the early 1870s, including the building of the steam mill, but it closed following a disasterous winter frost of 1883/84. Later some trials for copper were made here.

Remains There is much to see on this compact site, which is in reuse as a boatyard. The tiny mill with brick chimney, cottages and a delightful chapel-like structure with cast iron window frames. The slate-waste jetty is still in use, but the adit, which leads to a twll, is blocked by a fall. (21)

FRONHEULOG SN600998
Very small open working.
Remains Excavation only. (2)

GALLT Y GOG SH749014
Possible trial.
Remains Prominent waste heap and excavation. (47)

GARTHEINIOG SH822117
Pit/underground, operated 1880s to 1930s, connected by a short tramway to a mill served by the Hendre Ddu Tramroad. Output 1883 250 tons 9 men.
Remains Large pit accessed by upper adit, lower adit blocked. Worked into overhangs. In forestry there are possible vestiges of a tramway formation and incline that served the upper adit. A tramway formation can be traced from the lower adit past some machine bases to a mill building in reuse. This building, originally open-sided, has line shaft brackets. Behind is pipework for a turbine or Pelton wheel. There is a massive buttress at one end which is modern. The adjacent house is of much later date. The tramway link is unclear owing to forestry road construction. (54)

GARTH FACH SH634070
Almost certainly not slate.
Remains Excavation only. (14)

GERNOS SH669094
Trial?
Remains Slight excavation. (23)

GLANDYFI SN698961
A small working mainly producing slab. Opened in 1870s closed 1910. From a small mill at the adit, material was trammed across the river Melindwr to a cart loading point.
Remains Abutments of bridge but site much collapsed and obscured. (36)

GLYNIAGO SH719071
Very small underground working, trial only?
Remains In forestry. (41)

GWASTAD FRYN SH678098
Possible trial.
Remains In forestry. (28)

HENDRE SH682053 Trials?
Remains Excavation, possible adit. (31)

HENDRE DDU SH799125
Part underground, a fairly extensive site which had a substantial mill and other buildings but output unlikely to have exceeded 1000 tons pa (878 tons 31 men 1883). Operated from 1850s to 1940s. Material went out via the Hendre Ddu Tramway.
Remains Site mainly covered by forestry, workings on 4 levels, including a twll working. The compact mill area is cleared but there is a fine 2 storey building in reuse and the foundations of a number of other structures. There are three adits, the lowest, at mill level has some chambering. Above there is a second adit, flooded. Above is a third adit which leads to some chambering and to open workings. Above are the early open workings. At each adit level there are massive spoil heaps, notable for the size of many of the blocks. Tramroad formations, just traceable in forestry lead from each level to an incline down to the mill. There is a working, possibly just a trial adjacent to the head of incline. The main exit incline down to join the Hendre Ddu tramroad is obvious. There is a fine reservoir at the top of the site. (52)

HENDRE MEREDYDD = Gartheiniog.

LLECHWEDD SH670087
Possible trial.
Remains Ground disturbance. (24)

LLYN FANT SN717977
Small unmechanised underground working, material carted down valley.
Remains Little apart from the adit itself. Possible ruins of one small building. Some rail on the ground. There is a small underground trial at 718975 and an open working at 723975, both possibly associated with this site. (40)

MAES Y GAMFA SH818127
Modest pit working but with quite elaborate mill etc., seems to have produced ornamental blocks. Originally material was brought down by

incline to the mill, but as the working deepened blocks were run out on the level via a short tunnel. Opened 1888 closed 1914 (1898 22 men). An incline led to a branch of the Hendre Ddu Tramway.

Remains The only site in the valley to have substantial surface remains. Ruins of a mill (stone robbed to re-build Maes y Gamfa farm?). There is clear evidence of leatwork and rock-channelling to feed a breastshot mill-wheel. There are several other ruinous buildings and a drumhouse of substantial block construction that had a horizontal sheave, possibly it was a single acting trunk. Unusually there seems to have been a weighbridge with no house. The pit is accessed by a short tunnel, evidence of use of a channelling machine. There are parts for ornamental fireplaces in the mills area. At the head of the exit incline is a dwelling now in agricultural reuse. There are some traces of slate sleepers on the tramway formation between the mill area and head of incline. There are rollers, rail etc. from the exit incline in the river. (53)

MAES Y PANDY SH700089
Possible trial.
Remains In forestry, possible signs of disturbance. (37)

MINLLYN SH852139
An extensive site open and underground, in spite of its extent and it having, uniquely, a standard gauge rail link, output was not very large (1882 2830 tons 108 men). Substantially developed, on a pre-existing site in the 1870s, closed about 1916. Product mainly slab.

Initial workings were hillside quarries, later developed substantially but haphazardly underground. Material was reduced in a water turbine powered mill.

Later a large mill was built at valley floor level which reduced material from both the main workings and the several other dispersed workings on the site, described as having "40 Machines". A further short tramway took finished slate to Dinas Mawddwy station, terminus of the private Mawddwy Railway that made a junction with the main line near Cemaes Road.

All the tramways in site were of 2'4¼" ("half standard") gauge, an unusual dimension also used in the Glyn Valley.

Remains On the upper mills area is the very ruinous mill itself with a contiguous compressor house, workshops, weigh-houses, other buildings and traces of an extensive tramway network. The chimney is standing and in the adjacent boiler-house wall is the flue damper. The feed pipe for the turbine is in situ. There is a run of pillars possibly for compressed air piping. The formations of the long incline which brought material from Cae Abaty and the two shorter ones from the early open workings. A fine stone lined tramway tunnel leads through a pit to the main adit. Above this pit, near an incline head is a crane base. Underground there is extensive, but seemingly almost random chambering. There are several winches and much chain etc. as well as rail track. Near a flooded up working is a boiler, some machinery remnants and parts of what may have been pump gear. The engine, one assumes, pumped and wound. There is much evidence of pillar robbing and also of the use of channelling machines. The workings can also be entered by a sloping air shaft.

From the mills area, a tramway leads past some other buildings, small workings and an air shaft, to the head of the main incline down to the lower mill. On this incline there are, partially lost in forestry, tramways to other adits. One adit is open leading to a large chamber. This has some chains etc. and the fallen timbers of a bridge high above.

The lower mill is now in reuse by the woollen factory. Most of the station structures are intact. (62)

MORBEN SN715991
Possible trial.
Remains Some trace of excavation in forestry. (39)

NANT YR EIRA SH685088
A very small pit working, possibly only a trial.
Remains Excavation only. (32)

NANT YR ERYR SH735015
Almost certainly not slate.
Remains Working at roadside. (45)

NANT Y MYNACH SH643048
Possible trial.
Remains Traces of excavation. (15)

NAWLLYN SH732000
Almost certainly not slate.
Remains Possible digging. (44)

PANDY SH630029
Very small hillside quarry, possibly only producing block.
Remains Quarry area. The adjacent building was a fulling mill. (12)

PANT EIDAL SN652972
Small open working.
Remains Site now occupied by holiday home development which has obliterated any remains, but much slate on the site. (18)

PARC SH755005
Trial?
Remains Excavation only. (48)

PENNANT SH671097
Small hillside quarry, possibly only a trial.
Remains Excavation only. (25)

PEN Y BRYN SH706014
A small working, material being taken down a short incline to the road, where there may have been a mill. Later material was removed on the level by a tunnel. Operated by the Cae Graig Company around 1880, but may have been much earlier. Material carted to Pennal.
Remains Vestiges of incline and drumhouse, the tunnel is collapsed to surface for most of its length. Any buildings there may have been obliterated by a forestry road. (38)

PEN Y GRAIG SH872134
Trial?
Remains Traces of digging. (64)

PERFEDDNUANT SH630055
A small hillside working, deepened into a pit accessed by a short tunnel. All handworking. Slate conveyed to the main road by a cart track.
Remains Pit and tunnel. (13)

PONT FAEN SH763000
Pit, with mill and tipping area on opposite side of the road. Mill had 5 saws and 2 planers.
Remains Flooded pit. The mill area has been entirely cleared and a modern house built. Material was clearly originally moved across the road on the level. Not clear if there was any later, lower level access to avoid uphauling and pumping. The rubbish runs, being shallow are surprisingly long. (51)

RHYD YR ONNEN SH625017
Small underground working, probably operating in the late 1860s, closed after a roof fall. Material may have been carted to Talyllyn Railway.
Remains Nothing on the surface. The lower adit is collapsed, the upper adit is open but blocked inside by falls. There is a 'Jwmpah' jammed in a shot hole. (10)

RHAEADR SH682012
A tiny underground working lodged in a small gorge, probably used water power for sawing. Material taken away by cart.
Remains Just upstream of collapsed adit is a small building possibly a mill for one water powered saw. Slight vestige of a second building and a rubbish run with some rail on ground. There is also a massive square stone structure of unknown purpose.
Above the site are two breached dams in tandem. (30)

TAI NEWYDDION SH664062
Trial only?
Remains In forestry. (20)

TAL Y MIERYN SH831125
A small underground working, possibly unmechanised, connected to the Maes y Gamfa branch of the Hendre Ddu Tramway by a shallow incline. *Remains* Site now wooded, but some work traceable including the incline formation. (57)

TARGWRMOEL SH855148
Trial associated with Minllyn.
Remains In forestry. (63)

TY MAWR SH603005
Small open working. Local use only?
Remains Shallow excavation. (3)

TYN Y FACH SH675095
Tiny hillside quarry, possibly very early, for local use only.
Remains Excavation only. (26)

YR HORON SN600962
Two small hillside workings, mainly working shales for building, may have produced roofing slate at an early date.
Remains Pits. (1)

WYNNSTAY CASTLE SH844031
Small underground working.
Remains Two run-in adits in forestry. (59)

SECTION 12: CORRIS

Tal-y-llyn

Tywyn

Dolgellau

A 487

CORRIS

ABERLLEFENNI

Machynlleth

(DISUSED)
- - - - HORSE TRAMWAY
+++++++ NARROW GUAGE
STEAM RAILWAY

0 ————— 1 MILES

Corris Area Section 12

General

This area comprises those quarries on the route of the Corris Railway and its feeder lines. The area's development dates from the opening of that railway, but several quarries have a very long history of production and export. Although large quantities of roofing slates were produced, the area was, and certainly still is, mainly known for the quality of its slab.

Slate veins, of the Ordovician series, run east-west, the two best immediately north of Corris village and lesser ones some way to the south. As at Blaenau Ffestiniog, a number of workings, almost entirely underground, cluster around, dominating this one industry village.

As in most areas, the archaeology has suffered from landscaping, many surface remains have gone, but much of great interest survives.

Both in Corris itself and in Aberllefenni, the prolific and ingenious use of slate abounds and not only as a roofing and masonry material. In the former it is used, for instance, in place of cast-iron for coal-hole covers.

Transport

Obviously the 2'3"g Corris Railway is the main feature, all the quarries used it, either by branches, feeder tramways or, in a few cases, by carting to it.

Established in 1859 as a horse-drawn line it connected the quarries to a shipping point on the Dovey at Derwenlas, which was a long established shipping point for carted product. When the Cambrian Railway opened at Machynlleth in 1867, trans-shipment sidings were laid and the tramway south west of the town became disused. In 1879 the line was steamed, it remained in use until 1948.

The trackbed at the Aberllefenni terminus, opposite the Quarry mill, is obvious. It follows the road through the village, where at one point there is a particularly fine flight of slate steps. It then goes through fields to Corris where there is a nice bridge and part of the station buildings house a small museum. From Corris to the engine shed at Maespoeth about ½ mile distant, track has been relaid. From Maespoeth to about ½ mile short of Machynlleth, it can be almost continuously traced alongside the main road. There are several 'bus shelter' stations and one fine house, still in occupation. Vestiges of the branches to Cwm Eira and Llwyngwern can be seen.

After leaving the main road it cuts directly across fields to Machynlleth station, via the remains of the Dyfi bridge, whose collapse precipitated closure. Alongside the present Machynlleth station, some of the terminus buildings of the Corris Railway are in reuse. The bricked up arch where the main road passes under the railway denoted the path of the original tramway, which can be intermittently traced to the shipping point near Derwenlas.

There were 3 feeder tramways. The most important was the Upper Corris tramway which ran down the western bank of the river from Corris Uchaf. At Corris it passed close alongside the main road, north of the Aberllefenni turning, passing in a gulley between the road and houses, little accommodation bridges still being in use. Its trackbed now forms the Braich Goch hotel car park, from where it ran alongside the road to make a junction with the Corris Railway at Maespoeth. Much of it is traceable.

The most interesting branch was the Ratgoed tramway which ran from that quarry to make an end-on junction at Aberllefenni. Most of it remains, partly as a track and partly as a forestry road.

The remaining branch was the short line from the Aberllefenni quarry itself, to the Aberllefenni mill. It ran alongside the road and was in use, (latterly tractor powered) until the 1970s and in fact the trackwork outside the mill was not lifted until 1989.

1.	SH729082	Mynydd Tyn y Ceunant
2.	732088	Cwm Dylluan
3.	733070	Taran Cadlan
4.	738087	Tyddynberth
5.	739093	Llan y Groes
6.	744088	Tyn y Ceunant
7.	745066 etc.	Bryn Llwyd Uchaf
8.	745086	Gaewern
9.	746089	Abercwmeiddau
10.	748078	Braich Goch
11.	749029	Afon Dulais
12.	750085	Afon Deri
13.	754089	Abercorris
14.	757045	Llwyngwern
15.	759124	Y Waun
16.	760054	Rhiw'r Gwrelddyn
17.	760064	Cwm Era
18.	760081	Pandy
19.	760126	Vron Fraith
20.	761129	Waunllefenni
21.	762060	Ceinws Bach
22.	762132	Mynydd y Waun
23.	765101	Hen Gloddfa
24.	765108	Wenallt
25.	766062	Cwmodin
26.	766099	Ceunant Ddu
27.	768091	Matthews Mill
28.	768103	Aberllefenni

29.	777107 etc.	Cymerau
30.	787119	Ratgoed

ABERCORRIS SH754089

Open/underground.

Mid 19th C. Worked up to 1950s, with an output at the turn of the century of around 1000 tons pa with about 40 workers. Consisted of two hillside workings (the highest at well over 1000'), developed into pits accessed by tunnels, with some later underground working.

Material was lowered by incline to a mill's area some 600' below, the early mill was water powered, a later and larger mill was oil engine driven.

Originally access was by cart track, later by direct connection, via an incline to the Upper Corris Tramway.

Remains One adit to a pit has been tipped over, another, leading to underground workings is lost in forestry. One adit at a level above the head of incline is open, leading to some chambering, with a shaft for lowering material to the level below. A remote type drumhouse is at the top of the main incline with banksman's shelter on the crimp. Some rail and rope is on the ground. There is a small reservoir, partway down incline. Only traces remain of the original mill. The later, galvanised roofed, mill, has collapsed, also nearby, is a small ruined building and a hut. At a lower level, there are an office and dwellings in fair condition. Incline connection down to Upper Corris tramway just about traceable in the trees, the abutments of the bridge over Afon Deri, is at the incline bottom, near the present footbridge. (13)

AFON DULAIS SH749029

Underground, only a trial.

Remains Trace of possible adit. (11)

AFON DERI SH750085

Early pit/underground working.

Remains Collapsed adit, rubbish runs, ruins of a hut.

Possible incline alongside and overlaid by Abercorris incline. (12)

ABERCWMEIDDAU SH746089

Open/underground.

Hillside workings, opened in 1876, in 1882, 188 men produced 4173 tons. Material at first lowered by incline to a mill. As work developed material was brought out on the level by a locomotive worked tramway.

When workings deepened into a pit, the problems of uphaulage, rubbish disposal and pumping were solved in a radical manner, by boring a tunnel from pit bottom, which emerged at a point below the mill. A haulage incline was built and the mill wheel enlarged to power it. Good rock went up to the mill, rubbish was run out on a shelved tramway, which crossed the public road to a new tipping area. Finished product went down a short incline and over a bridge to the Upper Corris tramway. Some underground development was made from within the tunnel. Closed in 1905, but some small scale working since.

Remains The constricted nature of the site requiring high retaining walls to contain tipping are notable. At the quarry itself the prominent feature is the "Corris Binocular", twin tunnels machine bored in an abortive attempt to extend underground. (in the 1860s 2 boring machines were in trial use, a Hunter machine and a Cooke machine [which produced twin bores]). Rail hangs where these bores have been subsequently partly quarried away. The right-hand bore is only about 10 metres long the left-hand about 80 metres. There is a trace of another machine boring higher up. From the south-western corner of the pit a strike tunnel runs for some 120 meters to a fall. From the same point is the 250 metre drainage/access tunnel. Some slate sleepers are on the ground in the tunnel.

The original tramroad formation, at mills level passes some small buildings now in reuse, opposite them being a lavatory served by the nearby leat.

The mills area which stands on a massive platform is now almost entirely flattened. Sawn ends suggest use of Hunter saws.

Below this mill area, adjacent to the tunnel mouth, is the pit for the 50' wheel with part of the gearing and line shaft, which was some 15 feet below mill floor level. The uphaulage incline, serving the access tunnel is alongside and it is clear how the wheelpit was enlarged to provide extra power for it. There is a structure above the wheelpit to hold the haulage drum with internal stairs to allow for maintenance. On the far side of the old, upper tramway is the base for the return sheave.

The exit incline ran between high retaining walls, but these and the massive revetments, alongside the road, were lost in 1990 by landscaping. There is also a nice revetted platform for the rubbish tramway from the tunnel.

Above the mills area there are some small, early workings with possibly an incline down.

There is much fine dry-stone walling on a big scale and there were remarkable sets of cantilevered steps on site, but the best of them have disappeared. (9)

ABERLLEFENNI SH768103

Underground, with some early open working. Still in use.

Possibly dating from the early 16th C. it has worked almost continuously ever since. The slate now being worked does not readily split but yields a very high quality slab. Early workings were high on the hillside, with later workings at successively lower levels, the final adit being at valley floor level. Later underground working, by sinking down below this lowest adit level. An incline originally served almost the topmost levels, but as working progressed it was shortened as the lower levels were opened. Five drumhouses being successively used.

The original mill was adjacent to the foot of incline but in the late 19th C. a large mill was built at Aberllefenni village, near the terminus of the Corris Railway.

Rubbish disposal was a problem, the valley floor having to be used. Two water balanced inclines were employed to reach the top of the waste banks.

In 1883 158 men employed but this figure and the recorded output of 4814 tons, may have included quarries on the other side of valley, then in common ownership.

The Aberllefenni tramway which connected the quarry with the mill, remained in use until the 1970s, (although tractor powered since about 1950). It was thus the last survivor of the quarry tramways.

Remains There are several structures on the quarry site, some ruined, some still in use. The main items of interest are the water balances, one near the adit and one at the far side of the valley. Both are relatively complete, particularly the more distant one which has almost all pipework in situ (and, curiously, chains for holding down the drum).

The big incline, in its final, truncated, form is still in fair condition. It is a single-acting table incline with the counterbalance being provided by rubble filled box.

Underground, the working down from the highest level has produced 6/7 spectacular chambers some 600' high. The first two are abandoned and filled with water and rubbish to adit level. The third is being (late 1980s) worked some 100' below adit level by removing blocks with a chainsawing machine, resulting in a minimum of rubbish. Blocks are lifted to adit level by a crane and taken out by a diesel loco, for conveyance to the mill by bucket-tractor. Main tunnel continues on through abandoned chambers, upper tunnel (from head of truncated incline) emerges at far side of hill, where there are winches and a crane.

The reservoir to power the mill at the village, is a nice feature with its slate leats and sluices (it still provides water for cooling and washing). The dam is traversed by the trackbed of the Ratgoed tramway. There is a fine chapel-like building with a bell, that was once an office.

The mill, which once had 20 saw-tables, have been re-equipped with modern machines, including several diamond saws (including one giant ex Braich Goch machine of 4'3" capacity). There are also polishing and edging machines, some of which were brought from Caernarfon in 1988. Outside in its own building is a large horizontal, multiple frame saw, (unique to the industry). Some older machines and notable old lifting equipment is still in place.

There are nearby some interesting houses and cottages. (28)

BRAICH GOCH SH748078

Underground.

This was the largest and the oldest quarry in Corris itself. Very early users (1830s?) of sawing machines (Owen Owen hand operated). The first mill was on the hillside. Later, there was an extensive mills area, slate was brought, by a bridge over and also by a tunnel under, the old main road to this mills area. Output in 1882 5858 tons pa, 187 men. Mainly produced slab, being able to make very large sizes. There was direct connection to the Upper Corris tramway. For some years prior to the 1971 closure Gaewern material was reduced in the mill and reputedly some slab from Tyn y Ceunant.

Remains Shortly after closure the southern part of the site was landscaped, obliterating the mills area and all traces of the workings above (the main road now runs over the site of the mills). However on the oldest, northerly part there are traces of workings, some buildings and tramroad formations, including the surface connection to Gaewern. There may be adits in this area. There are some 15′ lengths of malleable iron T section rail with 5 "fishbellies" which may have come from Nantlle when that tramway was converted to standard gauge in 1867.

There is housing on the line of the old main road that may have had quarry associations.

Underground there are three adits open. No. 6, below road level, which in latter days was the main exit to the mills, which were at this level, divides left and right. The left leads to a partial collapse, the right penetrates some 1150 yards, past or looping through, several chambers. There are winch mountings, a steam winder, a portable lavatory and other minor artifacts. An incline down goes into floodwater and a close-timbered incline rises to Vanes level. A curiosity is, at the head of each incline is a signalling gong made of an old saw blade.

The No. 5 adit, immediately above, which at one time was connected to the mills area by a bridge over the then main road, runs left (SW) to a fall (hand winch in situ) and right (NE) to where a chamber that breaks out to bank may be entered, then continues to the incline.

The third and highest adit, is Vanes level which at one time served the old upper mill. This leads left to a collapse and right to several chambers, the penultimate has a steam winder, ("borrowed" from Aberllefenni shortly before closure!) and two hand winches, and various minor artifacts, there is rail and pointwork on ground. Nearby is part of a channeling machine and a lavatory.

These chambers, the last to be worked are under, and break into, Gaewern workings. A loop of this tunnel leads to the top of the fine, close-timbered incline, down to level 4, single-acting, built around 1950 (in 2 weeks working round-the-clock), to enable material to be taken out via 4 level. These workings, particularly near the head of the incline, are dangerous.

The present workshops and cafe are on ground built up on the old mills area. The trackbed of the Upper Corris Tramway forms a footpath to the east of the main road. (10)

BRYN LLWYD UCHAF SH745066 & 749072
Small trials on Braich Goch property.
Remains At 749072, an adit, open. (7)

CAMBRIA WYNN = Cwm Era. This name also is (erroneously) applied to Darren.

CEINWS BACH SH762060
Tiny open quarry.
Remains Working face. (21)

CEUNANT DDU SH766099
Underground.
Early working was mainly open. Material being removed by cart road. Later it was worked (in conjunction with Hen Gloddfa) entirely underground from an adit near valley floor level, material being reduced in Aberllefenni mill. The Hughes, treadle operated, trimmer was first used here.
Workings stated to connect through to Abercorris.
Remains Above valley floor level there are 5 levels. At the highest, level (No. 1), there are old open workings and a reservoir. Level 2, has an adit and a leat system including some fine slate troughing some 18″ wide by 4″ deep made of ¾″ thick slabs jointed together with ends rebated and sealed and reinforced by iron rod. There is tramroad connection to Hen Gloddfa and a remote type drumhouse, set well back with extended brake control. Level 3 is virtually quarried away, but there are some vestiges of buildings, including a drumhouse. Level 4 is largely tipped over. Level 5, has some ruined dressing sheds and, the curious feature of the site, a drumhouse with a drum made almost entirely of wood even to the brake drum. A fine example of the wheelwright's art.
The lowest adit at valley floor level dates from the time of combined operation with Hen Gloddfa.
In the early 1980s, a road was built to give access to the top of the site, and some untopping work was done. (26)

CWMBERGI = Wenallt.

CWM DYLLUAN SH732088
A small working in 2 pits, closed by 1876, it suffered from lack of transport facilities which would have been solved had the projected extension of the upper Corris Tramway been built.
Remains Site mostly in forestry. There is a stone-built incline with

an unusually massive remote drumhouse, some rubbish runs and a few small structures. (2)

CWM ERA SH760064

Open working, started in 1870s, employing about 50 men producing around 600 tons pa. Material trammed to the waterpowered mill at Escairgeiliog which was connected to the Corris Railway.

Remains Almost nothing on the quarry site itself, other than the incline formation and a tramway to the mill. The mill complex is intact and in reuse. The Corris Railway branch, with partly collapsed timber bridge, is obvious. (17)

CYMERAU SH777107 & 780116

Underground. A series of adits, mainly in two groups, with material being removed by cart. Later working used a water powered mill, uphauling from an adjacent adit. Ratcoed Tramway used. 1883 762 tons 29 men.

Remains There are some ruins of the mill and wheelpit, and the adjacent adit (flooded) that may have been uphauled by this same wheel. Cottages associated with the quarry are still in use. Up Valley 2 runs of adits (one open), incline and possible mill site. The reservoir and leatwork can be seen. (29)

CWMODIN SH766062

A small open, unmechanised, digging in a constricted little valley. Material removed via a short incline, by cart.

Remains Some rubbish runs and several collapsed adits that seem to have been unsuccessful trials. There is a curious drumhouse with an outcrop of rock forming one wall with the brakeman's platform cut into a ledge. This name locally used for Abercorris quarry. (25)

DARREN See Dovey Section 11.

ESCAIRGEILIOG = Cwm Era.

FOEL GROCHAN Alternative name of the older (upper) part of Aberllefenni, or, locally, the third (last to be worked) chamber of that quarry.

GAEWERN SH745086

Underground with some open working, it was established around 1820 and after connection, to the Upper Corris Tramway by an incline passing under the main road, developed considerably. By 1873 200 men were employed. In 1884 it merged with Braich Goch and later a tramway connection on the surface made to enable the Braich Goch mills to be used.

Remains Bulk working and road improvements have left little to be seen but there is an almost complete drumhouse and some building ruins. At the top of site there is a reservoir. Underground, the workings can be entered but are dangerous. (8)

HILLSBOROUGH = Tyddynberth.

HEN GLODDFA or *HEN CHWAREL* SH765101
Mainly underground but first working was by open quarrying with material being lowered by incline to valley floor to be carted away. Later worked in conjunction with Ceunant Ddu to which it was connected by a tramway. Last working by adit near valley floor level. Operations constrained by dispute that they were working Abercorris rock. Said even to have broken through into the latter's workings.

Remains At the highest level is a dressing floor with an extensive stock of slate, also some rail and trucks. A massive dry stone construction suggests that a ropeway was used from this level. There is a partly built drumhouse and table incline and the complete kit of Cast Iron parts (unused) for the making of a drum (Axle, Brakedrum [6' Dia], 2 Spiders and 1 Ring Spider [5' Dia]) and the Coalbrookdale Co. winch used to raise these heavy components.

Level 2 is largely lost in subsequent operations, but there are traces of a vertical shaft. Level 3 is lower limit of open quarrying, with an embanked tramroad towards Ceunant Ddu, to the head of a table incline apparently intended to be shared with that quarry, but possibly never completed. On level 4 at the bottom of the table incline, an embanked track runs south to curious drumhouse built into and effectively cutting a steep incline down from level 2. This forms a tiny remote-type drumhouse with a banksman's cabin alongside, with a brake adapted to suit the unusual juxtaposition. There is an adit, open, with rails in situ, at this level and some building remains.

At level 5, is another adit, nicely portalled, with some concrete bases adjacent, more buildings and close by the notable water balance put in by the Aberllefenni undertaking for disposal of their rubbish after they acquired the site. (23)

LLAN Y GROES SH739093
Possible trial.
Remains Slight excavation traces? (5)

LLWYNGWERN SH757045
Open quarry, some underground.
Developed in the early 1880s, it failed to fulfill early promise and output almost certainly never exceeded 1000 tons pa. (1883 915 tons 35 men). Material was removed from the original hillside quarry, by incline, to the mill. Later as the working deepened a level tramway led via a tunnel, to

the 30' water-wheel powered mill. Steam was introduced in the 1900s, with diesel later. An incline from the mill enabled loading onto a branch of the Corris Railway.

As overburden and the position of the reservoir limited the advance of the working face, the working was deepened into a pit with some chambering. It is clear that some extensive pit working and chambering was envisaged as a tunnel was bored from the foot of the exit incline, under the mill area to a point below the quarry. Although it did serve as a drain it was never employed as an exit route with, one assumes, uphaulage to the mill, or even the building of a new mill at a lower level.

At some time an attempt was made to develop a new operation above and remote from the main working and connected by a ropeway but this does not seem to have been a success. Some working went on until the early 1950s.

Remains The mill's area is now in reuse by the National Centre for Alternative Technology who make good use of many of the buildings. There is rail on the ground and some trucks and other artifacts are around. The main quarry may be reached by the access tunnel. Within are a number of platforms, a derrick and the base for a late haulage winch. There is some chambering on either side.

Above the access tunnel is the presumed lower mounting for the ropeway. At a higher level are rubbish runs and above again, the upper site with several ruined buildings and the upper mounting of the ropeway but the adit seems lost.

The reservoir is still in use as a water source. The drainage tunnel may be penetrated. The present car park is in the loading area for the Corris Railway branch, the abutments of the railway bridge across the Dulais can be seen and the high embanked approach causeway to it is a notable feature. (14)

MATTHEWS MILL SH768091?
Slate is said to have been sawn in this area prior to the building of mill at Aberllefenni. Possibly using an existing corn or fulling mill.
Remains Not identified. (27)

MYNYDD Y WAUN SH762132
Small open working.
Remains Excavation and tip. (22)

MYNYDD TYN Y CEUNANT SH729082
Possible trials.
Remains In forestry. (1)

PANDY SH760081
This was the start of an attempt to seek slate by tunneling south, abandoned at an early stage.

Remains Excavation and spoil. Wheelpit and some stonework of never completed surface structures. (18)

RATGOED SH787119

Earlier known as Alltgoed (and erroneously as Ralltgoed).
Mainly underground, opened in mid 19th C. Three mills operating at various times. Unfortunate lack of planning led to complicated working and movement of material. Output was small, 434 tons, 25 men in 1882. Closure in early 1950s.
Finished product was taken on the Ratgoed tramway to Aberllefenni. The tramway was the only link, apart from field paths, to the village that grew up around the quarry.
Remains Site now in forestry, parts being difficult to reach. At the highest part of site, above the forestry road, there is a small adit, possibly a late trial. Below is a large pit working, divided into three parts, accessed both by a cutting and by a tunnel (collapsed). There is an old, degraded incline (purpose not readily discernable), and an interesting flight of steps. Nearby are a number of buildings including a mill, possibly Pelton wheel or turbine driven, with some evidence of overhead shafting. This seems to have been the second mill to have been erected. There are several unidentified iron artifacts on the ground.
There is a main incline down from this level with unusual and complex brake gear with the band running in a flanged ring. The drum (7′ dia x 6′ long) is in two separate parts. All collapsed but virtually complete, including rope.
At an intermediate level is an adit (collapsed) which leads to chambering, which breaks out into the pit workings. An isolated rubbish run emerges from this adit, so if useful make came out, it may have been removed by the ropeway which was believed to have been used somewhere on this site, at some time.
At the foot of the upper main incline, a further incline runs down to valley floor level. The drum gear (also remote type) is similar, but although the brake has a shaft to couple up a second brake, and there is a spare band on the ground, there does not seem to have been space for a second brake drum. The remote brake lever was abandoned and replaced by a direct operating lever with a very crude wooden pin-down pillar.
At this level a tramroad leads to another mill, presumably the third to be built, some building foundations and a stocking area. This mill has the base of a late compressor and a most interesting, elaborately roofed stairway leading down to what was seemingly a Pelton wheel-pit.
There are several rubbish runs at this level emanating from an adit some 200 yards long, cut through country rock, with no workings but with 3 vertical shafts dropping from the chambering above. There is rail in situ. On either side of the lower main incline, near its foot are buildings, the northerly one seems to have been an old water mill adapted, possibly, as a workshop. The southerly one could have been a dwelling or barracks.

A lengthy abandoned incline had a horizontal sheave and, part way up, is a nice powder house. Another incline had a drumhouse curiously narrowed and another had an underfloor sheave.

There are several ruined buildings at valley floor level, including a mill, probably the first one built, with some evidence of underfloor shafting and embedded in the ground is the table of a saw-bench.

Close above this are some small workings, including an open adit, and a possible short incline.

There are the ruins of a number of cottages, a chapel and a manse. Ratgoed Hall, the owner's residence, is still in occupation. In front of the Hall is a most elaborately ornate stable block.

In forestry behind the lower mill are some extremely old workings, possibly going underground. High above the site is a reservoir. (30)

RHIW'R GWREIDDYN SH760054

Open quarry. Material was originally brought down to a water powered mill by inclines, but as the workings deepened it was hauled out on the level. Mill waste was tipped on the far side of the public road.

In spite of the relative proximity of the Corris Railway no connection was ever made.

Remains Little on the quarry site itself other than a weigh-bridge and a redundant drumhouse converted into a lean-to shelter. A fine range of mill buildings remain, some in reuse, one altered and extended in brick. There is a small reservoir, with piping to a turbine housing (which may have replaced a water-wheel). A covered channel carries the tailrace under the stocking area. (16)

RHOGNANT = Tyn y Ceunant.

TAL Y LLYN = Gaewern.

TARAN CADLAN SH733070
Reputed trial.
Remains In forestry. (3)

TROED YR ESCAIR = Cwmerau.

TYDDYNBERTH SH738087

Underground development in the early 1850s possibly from an earlier pit working, in anticipation of rail transport being available. Material was brought down by incline to a water powered mill. Successively owned by a series of promoters, The Great Welsh Union Slate Co. (1857), The Union Slate Co. (1859) and The British Slate Co. (1860), none of whom operated it. One assumes it was closed by the time the Upper Corris tramway opened in 1859 which accounts for the lack of any connection to it.

Remains In forestry, but at least one adit, some small building ruins,

188

traces of a reservoir and the incline formation are discernable.

Near the road is a fine range of buildings, now in reuse none really identifiable as the mill or the "Engine House" that is recorded on at least one prospectus as having been on site. A nearby row of cottages are named Hillsborough, the alternative name for this quarry. (4)

TYN Y CEUNANT SH744088

Partly underground, the smallest and furthest undertaking served by the Upper Corris tramway.

The workings were connected to road level by two inclines in tandem, there may have been a small waterpowered mill, probably prior to tramroad connection circa 1860. Latterly part of Braich Goch where, until the 1930s closure, material was brought for reduction.

Remains Little to be seen on the site itself apart from some vestiges of buildings and the incline formations. Adits are run in.

At road level, there are cottages possibly associated with the quarry, and the ruinous building is assumed to have been the small mill. (6)

VRON FRAITH SH760126

Two very small open pits, such material as was produced was carted via Aberllefenni.

Remains In forestry. (19)

WAUNLLEFENNI SH761129

Early small open pit.

Carted out via Aberllefenni.

Remains Vestiges of dressing sheds. (20)

WENALLT SH765108

Hillside terraces spectacularly developed on 9 levels with an incline down to valley floor where there was a water powered mill. Generally working on the south side with tipping on north side. Some tentative attempts to go underground. Open for only a few years around the 1880s, possibly used the Aberllefenni tramroad.

Remains A spectacular 5 pitch incline, now much degraded, is a main feature, with several ruined drumhouses, (2 and 3 from the top being remote type). Dressing sheds at the various levels. Some working above top of incline level.

At valley floor the mill is of great interest. It apparently contained 4 (or 4 pairs) of saw-tables driven by a shaft in a massive underfloor tunnel powered by a wheel behind and below the mill. There is a leat from a reservoir some distance up valley and a particularly fine tunnel taking the tailrace to the river. Nearby is a rake of attractive cottages with nice slate adornment round the windows and with some ornate sashes still intact. (24)

Y WAUN SH759124
Tiny scratchings.
Remains In forestry, possible excavation. (15)

Denbigh/Dinbych Area Section 13

General

This region comprised broadly four separate areas where there were a group of fairly substantial quarries, surrounded by outliners.

These groups were around Corwen, north of Llangollen, in the Glynceiriog valley and around the upper Tanat valley. There were other isolated occurrences, notably south of Denbigh town.

Silurian Series rock was worked and certainly in the case of Llangollen and Glynceiriog it was poor material, which readily degraded on exposure to weather.

Several of the quarries were ancient, eighteenth century or earlier. A number of the larger ones were underground.

Substantial remains are to be found at Penarth, Moelferna, Cambrian and Wynne (this last open to visitors), and much of interest at several others.

Transport

It is a diverse area and the transport arrangements are varied.

There was, unlike those in the Gwynedd areas, no sea-going transport but some did use canals. Some of the ancient sites in the east of the area, had a long history of cartage direct to markets in the English Midlands.

Those on the Horseshoe Pass, used the Llangollen canal. The Tanat Valley and Glynceiriog units used the Montgomeryshire Canal, and from the 1860s, the larger quarries used the main line railways.

From 1852 the stiff cartage down from the Horseshoe Pass was eased by the opening of the 3'g Oernant tramway. This is readily traceable from its end at Moel y Faen quarry, through Oernant and Berwyn quarries to the head of an incline. There are vestiges of a drumhouse and remnants of slate sleepers on the incline. From the foot of the incline, the line is then obvious partially as a lane, partly alongside the main road. There is a prominent embankment near the canal, which was crossed by a bridge to the Pentre Felin works where mill and other buildings are in reuse. The reduction of slate at the canalside was not a success as waste tipped into the river did not, as hoped, get washed away.

At Glynceiriog the Cambrian and Wynne quarry inclines were connected to the 2'4½" horsedrawn Glyn Valley tramway in 1873, which ran to the canalside at Gledrid, making use of a wharf and basin and part of the trackbed of an old colliery tramway. In 1888, it was diverted to make an interchange at Chirk station and steam introduced. The line closed in 1935. Most of the course is readily traceable.

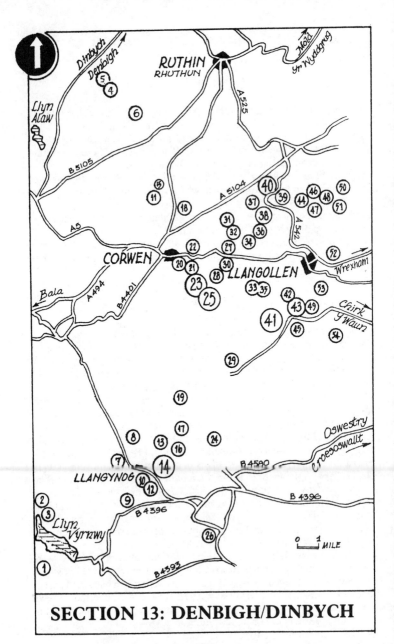

SECTION 13: DENBIGH/DINBYCH

After 1805 the Craig Rhiwarth and other Tanat valley quarries carted to the canal at Llanymynech, and from 1861 to the railway at the same place. When the Tanat Valley Railway was eventually opened in 1904, Craig Rhiwarth was able to make direct connection, and the neighbouring quarries had only a short cartage. Had this delightful railway been opened 30 or 40 years earlier, it might have had a dramatic effect on the fortunes of slate in the valley. It closed 1967, and is easily traceable over its entire length.

The only quarries to effectively use direct connection to the rail network were Penarth and Deeside/Moel Ferna. The 1863 line to Corwen (later to Dolgellau), enabled their rapid development, each having connection to interchange sidings. The former by incline, but the latter by the fascinating Deeside Tramway. Opened around 1870, it must have been one of the last wooden railed tramways in Europe. 2'6"g, it was gravity powered, empty wagons being brought up by horses each morning. Originally running from Deeside quarry to Glyndyfrdwy station, via the Nant y Pandy mill, it was later extended (wtih steel track), to Moelferna quarry. It remained in use until the 1940s.

Most of the route is readily traceable. The intermediate incline, immediately above Deeside quarry, still has its horizontal sheavegear, remotely mounted in a block housing. In the vicinity of Nant y Pandy mill there is some wooden rail (with steel sheathing missing) on the ground, and several examples of the iron tie-rods around.

Near the main road, the drumhouse of the final incline still stands, but the horizontal sheave gear was removed to Bwlch Gwyn, near Wrexham in the late 1970s.

1.	SH959208	Afon Hirddu
2.	965250	Afon Nadroedd
3.	968243	Nant Alltforgan
4.	977594	Aber
5.	978598	Nantglyn
6.	SJ 031546	Nilig
7.	041271	Glanyrafon
8.	042291	Bwlchgwyn
9.	044229	Clochnant
10.	047262	Craig y Cribin
11.	048478	Clegir
12.	049259	West Llangynog
13.	051289	Llwyn Onn
14.	053263	Craig Rhiwarth
15.	065481	Wernddu
16.	066274 etc.	Craig Glanhafon
17.	074294	Powis
18.	074464	Tyn y Rhos
19.	075326	Cwmmaengwynedd

20.	081434	Corwen
21.	085434	Colomendy
22.	088444	Caer Derwen
23.	107424	Penarth
24.	124285	Mynydd Mawr
25.	125399	Moelferna
26.	126223	Brithdir
27.	130442	Coed Tir Llannerch
28.	138404	Deeside
29.	141327	Sarphle
30.	148417	Nant y Pandy Mill
31.	157453	Cwm Tydi
32.	160448	Mynydd Bychan
33.	161398	Glyndyfrdwy
34.	162448	Cymmo
35.	166384	Nantyr
36.	169453	Rhiw Goch
37.	171478	Craig y Glem
38.	185463	Berwyn
39.	185469	Oernant
40.	185477	Moel y Faen
41.	189378	Cambrian
42.	199385	Bryn Eithin
43.	199379	Wynne
44.	202473	Craig Wynnstay
45.	206377	Tydraw
46.	208476	Ffynnon y Gog
47.	210469	Foel
48.	210471	Abergwern
49.	215382	Pen y Bryn
50.	215478	Pant Glas
51.	216472	Eglwyseg
52.	218436	Pentrefelin Mill
53.	230400	Craig y Dduallt
54.	234362	Craig yr Orin

ABER SH977594

A small and very primitive and shallow open working, producing slab. Hand sawing, allegedly used right up to 1920s closure, although site examination shows that mechanical sawing was used at some time. It seems unlikely that rails were ever used on this site.

Remains Shallow pit, partly backfilled with rubbish, with vestiges of a number of tiny buildings, most characterised by tiny alcoves. To the south west, in forestry, is a trace of a low dam, downstream of which is a curious little building that could have housed a Pelton wheel, (although the water head seems inadequate), with possible pipe saddles behind it. In front of this is a floor about 15′x4′ consisting of 3 massive slabs 4′8″ x 4′ divided and edged by slate kerbs. In front again is what could have been an open-fronted working shed. Whilst sawn ends in the quarry itself were hand-sawn, those around this latter area were cut by a mechanical sand-saw (many are oddly bevelled). It therefore seems that there was a power sand-saw(s) on this base. This area was connected to the quarry site by a cart track. Material left the site by cart road. (4)

ABERGWERN SJ210471
Small hillside quarry, carting to road. Closed end 19th. C.
Remains Access tunnel (blocked) small dressing shed and other buildings, access track. Also at 210469. Now in forestry. (48)

AFON HIRDDU SH959208
Tiny open working circa 1830.
Remains Excavation and access track. (1)

AFON NADROEDD SH965250
Underground.
Remains In forestry — adit collapsed. (2)

BERWYN SJ185463
A shallow open hilltop working covering an extensive area, material brought by a short incline to a mill. Originally, finished product, mainly slab, was dispatched by an incline down to the road, but later the Oernant tramroad, ran through the mill area, and so served the quarry.
1892 inventory showed only machine as being one planer, (all sawing done by hand?). Handsawing allegedly used as late as 1960s.
In use on very small scale in 1980s.
Remains Little to be seen on the actual quarry site apart from traces of tiny buildings. The mill, now largely a sheet iron structure is still in use with a traditional saw-table converted to overhead type (diamond), there are other saws, planers etc. Among the other buildings is a two-storey office. The old incline is a clear feature. The present access road runs partly on the Oernant tramway trackbed.
There are excavations at 193461 which are believed to have been associated with this quarry, worked in mid 19th C. (38)

BRITHDIR SJ126223
Slate extraction at least proposed, here in 1880 and machinery bought.
Remains Pit, possible rubbish run. (26)

BRYN EITHIN SJ199385
Open pit possibly very old.
Remains Excavation. (42)

BWLCH GWYN SJ042291
Possibly only a trial.
Remains Excavation. (8)

CAER DERWEN SJ088444
Trial.
Remains Excavation. (22)

CAMBRIAN SJ189378
Open pit workings, later underground. Possibly dating from 17th C., a company was formed in 1857 to exploit the workings and substantial developments followed the opening of the Glyn Valley tramroad in 1873. The piecemeal original layout, the necessity to uphaul rubbish (due to constraints of the site), the faulted geology and the poorness of the slate, made working difficult.

The 1870s work included the driving of a drainage tunnel from the most north-westerly pit, under 3 other principal pits to point lower down the hillside.

In the late 1890s underground extraction commenced, by chambering off of and below the drainage tunnel. Also by extending the tunnel north-west and chambering off it and on two levels above it.

Locomotive haulage was used in this main, and some branch, tunnels (finally over ½ mile long).

Originally, dressing was carried out adjacent to the diggings, but after the full development of the main tunnel for haulage and drainage, reduction was done in a mill near the tunnel mouth. Although product could be conveniently dispatched along the main tunnel, restricted tipping space meant that much rubbish still had to be uphauled.

There seems to have been a minimum of sawing done, and up to 1870s there was only one mill (water-powered, adjacent to and serving the Chwarel Ucha).

Material was crewled 3 wagons at a time down a 2'4¼"g incline to the Glyn Valley tramroad at Glyn Ceiriog.

Peak output c. 4000 tpa. Closed in 1947, (when men went on snow clearance for the council and did not return), but little work after 1938, the Glyn Valley tramroad having closed in 1935.

Remains The whole site is afforested and demolition and the highly degradable nature of the material has left few surface buildings. (A rabbit has burrowed into one substantial slate slab anchorage block!) Even much of the very extensive spoil has become so poor that trees flourish.

To the NW of the byroad that skirts the top of the site, adjacent to the reservoir, a haulage incline emerges from underground chambers. (These are flooded rather than draining down to the tunnel, due to falls below). There are the remains of an engine house and traces of a weighbridge. This incline appears only to have been used for rubbish.

Immediately within the loop of the road, is the pit of Martins quarry (the road was resited in February 1878 to allow enlargement of this pit). Earlier known as Chwarel Ucha, it was a hillside quarry, intensively developed by the 1857 company. Almost no trace remains of the buildings which were to the NE of this pit, as, apart from recent demolitions, the water-powered mill etc. were on ground quarried away after the 1870s. In the pit are the remains of an engine-house, an air-receiver, cranks and other compressor parts and a possible coal bin. Also a frame of an incline trunk. A much degraded incline formation leads steeply upwards. This was almost certainly used only for waste disposal. (Siting a steam engine at the foot of incline would suit the ready availability of fuel via the main tunnel). A compressor seem to have been substituted for a winder after the incline was abandoned.

At quarry bottom (at original mid 1870s level) is a tramway cutting on the line of the main tunnel, (now a watercourse), with an adit at either end. The NW adit, below the incline mentioned above, (late 1890s work?) leads to chambering, with the tunnel ending in a fall-blockage, but there was chambering above and possibly below. There are the frames of 2 trunk-incline carriages, a rusting body nearby of similar size suggests a tank for water-balancing, presumably to lift rubbish internally. There are parts of a hand-pump and a "2 seater" lavatory.

The SE adit, which is the start of the main drainage tunnel, also leads to chambering. Immediately inside there are 2 triangular wooden structures presumably belonging to the incline trunk frames in the NW tunnel, (washed downstream by water?)

Within the convoluted chambering, with evidence of 'cupboarding' and pillar robbing, is a flooded incline down, with at its head a substantial engine mounting, possibly air driven. Another chamber contains the mounting and earthenware supply pipes for a Pelton wheel for driving a compressor. Discarded saw-blades have been used as "washers" for rods bracing the masonry mounting. A further chamber breaks out up into the next pit, Townsend quarry. Opened in about 1877 it originally drained down into the main tunnel by a vertical shaft, a place where the tunnel roof has been shuttered might be the base of this shaft. Within this open chamber is a well-preserved "caban" and an iron vessel that may have been a boiler or an air-receiver. This is alongside a mounting for a haulage engine which powered, either by steam or air, an uphaulage incline. The mountings in the chamber, and on the surface above and the absence of a prepared formation, suggest that it was a rope or chain incline.

On the main tunnel there is some heavy rail and proper weighted-lever points, appropriate to locomotive working, but several parts of the workings seem to have been inaccessible to rail track.

Continuing along the main tunnel, one passes a side tunnel concrete-plugged with a valve, which apparently connects to the flooded Dennis quarry (named after the engineer). There are some signs from here on of a trench in the tunnel floor that could have accommodated a pipe. This pit, also an 1870s development, is in two parts both flooded and in one there is a sunken boat. A short tunnel, well above water level connects them. Both waste and good rock seems to have been removed by 2 tunnels to the south (not traceable), and by a shaft sunk to main tunnel level. No waste seem to have been uphauled from this pit.

The various buildings to the south of the pit, have all but vanished but the tree-covered rubbish runs are prominent.

The final pit on the main tunnel is McEwens quarry, formerly known as Old Quarry one of the ancient workings, of which there are several about the site, it was actively worked after 1857. It is on a side-loop of the main tunnel and it seems that this main tunnel was an extension of a tunnel originally serving only this pit. The original, early access to this pit was by a cutting and then possibly by some kind of uphaulage now quarried away. It does not seem that after the adit access was available that spoil was uphauled from this pit.

Shortly after McEwens the tunnel has been culverted for its final 30 yards to adit mouth by a 3' dia. concrete pipe.

There are few traces of the mill (Pelton wheel powered?) and other buildings that were between the adit mouth and the main exit incline but one structure is possibly built from stone "robbed" from the old buildings. The head of incline is obscure, but it may be traced descending to the village. Adjacent to head of incline are considerable rubbish runs. (41)

CHWAREL GRAIG = Penarth.

CLEGIR SJ048478
A small face working yielding a very pale coloured slate, opened in 1870s.
Remains Almost none apart from working itself and track out through a farm. (11)

CLOCHNANT SJ044229
Very small underground.
Remains 2 adits, one to open shaft above. Dressing shed.

CLOGAU = Berwyn.

COED TIR LLANNERCH SJ130442
Small open working.
Remains Rubbish runs. (27)

COLOMENDY SJ085434
Around beginning of 20th C. producing "coarse slate", very small, reported as working "inside" i.e. underground, 1924.
Remains In forestry. (21)

CORWEN (or Corwen Stone) SJ081434
Possibly building stone only. Name Corwen also applied to Penarth quarry.
Remains Possible excavations. (20)

CRAIG RHIWARTH SJ053263
Hillside quarry, part underground. Opened before 1760, possibly 16th C. Material from early workings sledged down to valley floor some 800' below. (Aitken account 1797.) Very active in first decade of 19th C. when an incline was installed. This incline was replaced by another further west during mid 19th C. development. Further galleries were opened up and an extensive 2' gauge tramway system laid down. Later working was underground. Output 1856 1000 tons, 1864 40 men, 1882 329 tons 15 men, 1885 40 men.

Material was carted possibly for river carriage, later to the canal at Llanymynech, and after 1871 to the railhead at Porth-y-waen.

After declining during the latter years of the 19th C., there was some temporary revival following opening of the Tanat Valley Railway. When the Tanat Valley Railway was opened the incline was extended under the road to exchange sidings at the terminus. There was some very limited activity in the 1930s when men moved here after the closure of West Llangynog. Then an oil engine used (for winching and generating?), trimming was by a Greaves treadle operated machine. Final closure in 1940.

Remains The salient feature is the main incline at the foot of which are traces of the old cartage wharf. The tunnel under the road is lost but there are vestiges of the exchange siding area and a possible trimming shed or small mill behind the present cafe. At the head of incline with the remains of the drum gear, (unusually, the spiders being in 2 halves), is a drumhouse with an adjoining workshop. To the west a track leads to a powder house. To the east the tramway formation is benched out of the steep hillside to reach some dressing sheds and the foot of a short incline. At the head of the incline is a drumhouse (remote type, as are most on site) with the remains of gear, some buildings and a modernish steel stanchion of unknown purpose. Chambers here are open and a hand winch, headframe, railtrack etc. inside, suggest that this was a late working.

From the top of this incline the tramway continues to the foot of another incline. Part way up is a level with some, possibly early, chambering. At the top is a working area with various buildings, including a drumhouse, with most curious flat bar tie-rods and a trimming shed with a neat aperture to allow trimmings to fall down the mountainside. There are the much degraded remains of another incline above this and some rather confused workings and structures, possibly abandoned at an early date. There are workings, clearly unconnected to any incline system higher up and also some further east at a slightly lower level. These are possibly where the quarry was first worked.

Below is a path system which may have been the old sledgeway. There are also structures that suggest a ropeway from the lowest working level to this path (this could be the original first-built "incline" as there is no trace of any incline down the mountain other than the obvious one). (14)

CRAIG WYNNSTAY SJ202473
Small pit working opened 1886 with 30 men, clearly fewer later, closed early 1900s.
Remains Access tunnel (blocked), small building remains, access track. (44)

CRAIG Y CRIBIN SJ047262
A small hillside/underground working dating from mid 19th C. Closed in 1880s. It was briefly re-opened in the 1930s. There was a short self-acting incline to the road.
Remains Dressing sheds, a great deal of stock (including flags) on ground, chambers accessible at 2 points. Powder house lower down hill. (10)

CRAIG Y DDUALLT SJ230400
Small, possibly mid 19th C. working.
Remains Excavation. (53)

CRAIG Y FOEL = Foel.

CRAIG Y GLEM SJ171478
A hillside/pit working, mainly slab. Had a steep powered incline, possibly steam with the same engine powering saws, (later i.c. powered?). Road access. Operated 1870s-80s, revived 1890s closed 1940s.
Remains Tips used as a source of bulk fill and the pit fully tipped into, almost nothing remains. Vestige of top of haulage incline and some concrete machines bases. (37)

CRAIG YR ORIN SJ234362
Pit with some underground. In the 18th C. was recording 300-600 tpa of slates plus slab in 1790s, seems to have declined after this and possibly only sporadically worked. 1887 55 tons 2/3 men.
Remains Some small buildings, tunnel under road, possible drumhouse and incline, very limited underground chambering, access track. (54)

CRAIG Y PISTYLL = Powis.

CRAIG GLANHAFON SJ066274
Small pit/underground workings, worked early 20th C.
Remains Excavations and tips. Adit and run-in shafts. (16)

CWMMAENGWYNEDD SJ075326

Originally open, then underground.

Operated 3 phases 1867-71, 1876-86, 1899-1910. Apart from '06/07 when there were up to 20 men employed, manning averaged approximately 4. Originally worked the exposed outcrop, with some attempt to go underground, then slightly lower down further open working, subsequently underground with trimming and handsawing on site. Then finally, on a lower level, more substantial underground working via a long tunnel with (possibly 1906) the construction of a tramway, incline, mill and reservoir.

Suffered from lack of communications. There were at least two proposals for a railway up the valley but apart from post 1904, when a traction engine towed trailers to Llanrhaeadr-ym-Mochnant, product had to be carted to the railway at Porth-y-waen. Peak output 1876 50 tons 6 men, but usually a tiny fraction of this.

Remains At the top of the site are the original open workings with an abortive tunnel, (open). There was circular sawing (hand powered?), there are vestiges of a building that might have housed such a machine. Slightly lower down is a further working with a possible adit (collapsed) and another (open) which divides to some limited chambering. Bar rail directly tenoned into sleepers, is in situ and a quantity of aluminium tube unconnected with quarrying. Part-way along the tunnel is a side-cutting (now banked with off cuts and rubbish) the presence of sawn ends outside and in the tunnel up to this point, together with the absence of any building strongly suggests that hand-powered circular sawing was done, here, underground. Shot holes do not appear to be machine drilled. There is one large block and a number of slabs underground.

Adjacent to these workings is a building, domestic and/or forge with a shaft with gears that might be part of a saw-table drive. No slate work done in or around this building. From this area a cart track leads out.

Lower down is the 'main' adit (collapsed) and adjacent are traces of a building, either the forge or the office that were both near this adit. There was apparently also a small water-wheel to drive a ventilation fan but no trace remains. Above is a depression with traces of walling which may have been a reservoir, with a run-in ventilation shaft nearby. A tramway formation leads to a drumhouse with an uncommon, 4 spider drum by Turner of Newtown. One pillar carries the initials D.P.LL. (D.P. Lloyd was manager 1906). The incline forms a forestry firebreak. At the foot of incline are the pillars of a tramway bridge leading to a mills area and traces of a Pelton wheel powered mill building which lacked a fourth wall. Possibly other buildings also and a loading bank.

Uphill there is a fine granite dam and a powder house. Nearby is a ruin of a rake of four barracks or cottages.

At the edge of the forestry below the dam are two spoil runs, one to a run-in adit, the other to a 30' deep cutting that does not appear to have gone underground, both apparently abortive. (19)

CYMMO SJ162448
Two very tiny workings on either side of a hilltop.
Remains Traces of a dressing shed. (34)

CWM-TYDI SJ157453
Very small, part underground, possibly a trial only.
Remains Run-in adit, spoil heap. (31)

DEESIDE SJ138404
Open hillside working developed in the 1840s (or later?) with a substantial water powered mill complex at Nant-y-Pandy (148417). Connection to the mill was by the 2′6″ gauge wooden railed Deeside tramway. In the 1870s this was extended, in steel to the Moelferna quarry. The tramway continued, via a table incline to Glyndyfrdwy station where there was a massive wooden gantry to facilitate trans-shipment of slab which was the main product.

The quarry closed in the 1920s, but the tramway continued to serve Moelferna until 1930s. Apart from being one of the last such railways laid down it was undoubtedly one of the last to close.

Remains Very little to be seen at the quarry site apart from some slight vestiges of small buildings. The incline which was operating in 1872 has been entirely quarried away. The incline carrying the tramway extension to Moelferna has remote type horizontal sheaves common in this area. The tramway formation is reasonably intact for much of its length. Some of the wooden rail is still on the ground complete with iron tie rods, but the iron sheathing has been removed. There are some nice embankments and cuttings. At Glandyfrdwy the house now in reuse near the incline head was the quarry office. (28)

DEESIDE SLAB WORKS = Nant y Pandy Mill.

EGLWYSEG SJ216472
Tiny working possibly only a trial.
Remains In forestry, vestiges of access track. (51)

FOEL SJ210469
Tiny hillside working.
Remains Now in forestry, some buildings. (47)

FOEL FORYDD = Mynydd Bychan.

FFYNNON Y GOG SJ208476
Hillside quarry.
Remains Almost everything destroyed by forestry and roadworks. (46)

GLANYRAFON SJ041271
Underground.
Remains Traces of dressing sheds, deep shafts, adit near road open but flooded. (7)

GLYNDYFRDWY SJ161398
Small open working, operating at least 2 separate periods. Cart road to Glyndyfrdwy.
Remains Dressing sheds and rubbish runs. (33)

HAFOD Y GWYNFE = Tydraw? Working in 1751.

LLANDDERFEL = Cletwr.

LLECHWEDD GWYN SJ20x34x also
SPRING HILL Not identified.
Stated to be working on a small scale in 1920s. Farms of these names.

LLWYN ONN SJ051289
Tiny digging.
Remains Excavation. (13)

MOELFERNA SJ125399
An almost entirely underground working opened in the 1860s, a substantial producer of roofing slate occasionally exceeding 6000 tons pa. Adits were on 7 levels, with a large, steam, later i.c., powered mill. A gas engine installed in 1912, diesel in 1926, electricity by 1920, diamond saws 1926. Originally material carted by the road which now gives access to site. After 1872 a table incline originally only up to 3 level, was extended to 6. This connected the levels and also lowered finished product to the Deeside tramway which was extended southwards (in conventional steel track) to serve this site. Wagons travelled down by gravity in journeys under the control of a riding brakeman, empties being returned daily by horses. The Nant y Pandy mills were not used. Closed 1960.
Remains On upper level, an adit and a building of unclear purpose but a plummer block suggests machinery was installed. There is a weighbridge, a remote type drumhouse which housed horizontal sheavegear and the remains of an incline table.
At intermediate level, an adit, weigh-house, a double rake of buildings which may have been a barracks also two massive pillars which supported the gantry which may have been for transferring wagons from 2′g to 2′6″g. Apparently the narrower gauge was used underground with the wider, tramway, gauge also being used on the surface.
At lowest level, a further adit, a large stockyard, weigh-house, offices etc., powder house and a mill. The construction of the mill is unusual, fairly crude walling with cgi roof and along one side a sort of lean-to with sloping

walls giving a buttressing effect. This large lean-to seems to have had very restricted access into the main mill itself. At one end of the mill is a massive concrete base for an oil engine.

There are a very large number of collapsed dressing sheds, besides many which have been tipped over.

Underground, there is much chambering on several levels, but since all adits were closed on abandonment, access is difficult. On level 4, there is an intact bridge over workings below. Above this, levels 5 and 6 and levels 6 and 7 were connected by underground gravity inclines. They both have rollers in site but no rail. The 5/6 drum is intact but on the ground, the 6/7 incline drum is still in its mounting.

On level 6 there is a massive wooden, coal-mine type "cog" supporting the roof of a chamber. (Men from the Wrexham area, with coal-mining experience may have been employed.) There are various artifacts including winch frames and a hand pump. There are several air doors and a ventilation shaft rises to bank from level 7. (25)

MOEL Y FAEN SJ185477

Possibly of 17th C. origin. Open workings of considerable extent with some underground. An east-west vein, dipping steeply to north was worked.

Mainly developed following connection to the Llangollen canal by an extension of the Oernant tramway in the 1857. (1882 2380 tons 84 men.) After closure of the tramway, lorries were used to convey to Llangollen station. Closed in 1940s following some years of very limited working.

Remains Three main workings, deepended into pits, with some intermediate hillside working. The largest, (easterly) pit has vestiges of dressing sheds, (some of the very large number on site), at the highest (original hillside working) level. Lower down is cutting access, with an incline down with some slate sleepers on the ground and further dressing sheds and a weighbridge. Lower again is a run-in adit, and still lower, roughly at pit-bottom level is a further run-in adit.

The upper adit is open at the pit end, where there are two entrances. Inside there is rail on the ground and some attempt at chambering. There has been much rock-fall inside the pit all but obscuring the floor. Part way down there are several places where a line of chambering on the north side from pit-floor level has broken out. These are inaccessible and presumably connect to the run-in lower adit.

The middle pit, partly water filled, has a slot access with traces of what may have been a winding house for a chain or rope incline. The cutting to the run-in access adit, to a lower level is a clear feature.

The westernmost pit, partly water filled, is at a slightly lower level and has the foundations of what may have been a steam winding house and/or sawing mill.

The mill area is much disturbed and little remains apart from a free-standing smithy hearth and the foundations of several buildings. To the north is a row of cottages, still in occupation which were built for workers use.

The line of the Oernant tramway, with some slate sleepers in situ, is clearly traceable. (40)

MYNYDD BYCHAN SJ160448
A tiny hillside quarry that mainly produced block.
Remains Ruins of a tiny shed and some trimmings suggest the possibility of roofing slate being made. (32)

MYNYDD MAWR SJ124285
Very small. Possibly not slate.
Remains Some excavation. (24)

NANT ALLTFORGAN SH969243
Hillside quarry on steep site.
Remains Waliau and rubbish runs.

NANTGLYN SH978598
Extensive shallow working for slab mainly for local use, all hand-sawing. closed 1950s. At one time a tramway connection was proposed.
Remains Very shallow working face. Some vestiges of small buildings. (5)

NANT GWRYD = Craig yr Orin?

NANTYR SJ166384
A small pit working operating in mid 19th C. Had the hoped for extension of the Glyn Valley Tramroad been made, expansion might have taken place. Owned by Cambrian company.
Remains Main pit is now an ornamental pond with site forming a picnic area. (35)

NANT Y PANDY SJ148417
The mill for Deeside quarry. Sited here to take advantage of abundant water power. It is reputed to have closed by 1914, several years before the quarry ceased. It is not clear where reduction was then carried out.
Remains The substantial buildings are extensive and apart from being roofless are in fair condition. There is the pit for a 30′ wheel and its associated launder pillars, a mill which contained planers and sand-saws. There are several other structures, including a possible office, stable, and formations of a tramway network with two bridges. Nearby is a small reservoir and some neat leatwork. (30)

NILIG SJ031546
Small open working.
Remains Excavation only. (6)

OERNANT SJ185469

A hillside working, mainly slab although roofing slate said to have been produced in 17th C. Some slab sawing on site. The Oernant tramway was laid through the site in the 1860s, conveying material to a mill at Pentrefelin on the canalside near Llangollen.

Remains The original working is in trees below the main road and the working area has buildings in agricultural use which may have been adapted from the quarry buildings.

The later and larger working above the main road is much disturbed by bulk fill removal etc. (39)

PANT GLAS SJ215478

Elongated hillside working, material taken to a mill by an incline. Output in 1883 735 tons 35 men. Closed about 1920.

Remains Some vestiges of buildings, drumhouse and incline to possible mill building now in reuse. Possible collapsed tunnel in workings. (50)

PENARTH SJ107424

A moderate sized quarry, initially terraces and open pit but later underground. Generally dated as from 1868 when development took place, with the arrival of the railway, but some open workings are undoubtedly much older. The initial working used hand dressing and carted to the road. Water power may have been used after the mid 19th C. underground development. In or shortly after 1868 150 men said to be employed but only 10 men recorded for 1883, but with a creditable near 500 tons of production. Closed in 1890 but reopened five years later.

An incline connection was made to the railway. Near the foot of this incline was a sawmill (waterpowered?) which may have had sandsaws. It is stated that in 1903 all sawing was done in this "Wharf" mill.

In 1904 a sawing shed opened at the eastern end of the site with a 12hp Blackburne engine. Possibly later than this a Hornsby 40hp gas engine was installed, which is stated to have operated a "force pump". Possibly before a lower adit provided drainage (and some outlet for rubbish). These ic engines may have replaced steam.

In the years before closure in the 1932 only slab (about 1000 tons pa) was produced.

Remains There are a number of buildings on site. The mill contains remnants of shafting, pulleys etc. and at one end there is motor room bearing the date 190? There are remnants of a big, open-air horizontal gang saw with carriage and alongside it, concrete machine bases. The nearby adit has been blocked and internally dammed to provide a limited water supply (for saws?). On the ground outside are the remains of the producer-gas plant. Near the drainage/rubbish adit is a weigh-house containing mechanism.

The main incline is an obvious feature with its unusual drumhouse which is a shallow construction in the rock above and behind the incline head that must have almost totally enclosed the horizontal sheave gear which was connected to a brake cabin by a rod. (Somewhat similar to the gear at Moelferna.) Much of this mechanism is in situ including traces of a remote controlled crimp sprag. There are traces of what may have been an incline table.

Where the incline passed under the main road is now denoted by a culvert. Nearby are some vestiges of the 'Wharf' mill.

There are a number of small artifacts around the site, including sand-saw blades. No trace has been found of the use of water power.

In the pit, where the underground workings break out to bank, there is a stock of old make of moss-slate type. Behind there are the old and quite extensive terrace workings, with ruinous dressing sheds etc. and a considerable stock of, much degraded, product. There was a multi-pitch incline system here, stated to have horizontal sheaves, but little, if any trace now remains.

Above the pit are traces of a small block-making operation using country rock. It is believed that in the early years of the century rock may have been sent to Llanfair quarry (Section 9) for crushing.

Underground there are extensive tunnels on 3 levels, with much rail on the ground and at least one incline with rail in situ. There are several winches and other items. The chambering system appears to exploit 2 veins. (23)

PENTREFELIN SJ218436
A slateworks on a canal wharf. Waterpowered it dealt with material brought from the Horseshoe Pass quarries by the Oernant tramway. Dating from the 1840s, it had, at one time, 8 planers, 3 circular saws and a sand-polisher operated by a 18'x4' water-wheel, it continued in use, despite waste tipping problems resulting from complaints about blocking the river, until the 1920s.
Remains Buildings (in reuse), canal wharf, railway loading point, leatwork. (52)

PEN Y BRYN SJ215382
Slab quarry, working in 1870s.
Remains Excavation. (49)

PEN Y GLOG = Penarth.

PISTYLL = Powis.

POWIS SJ074294
A small hillside quarry, with possibly some underground working, operating around 1880, perhaps much earlier. Material lowered by an incline to a mill. Cart transport.
Remains Quarry face, some traces of incline, mill site. (17)

RHAEADR = Powis.

RHIW GOCH SJ169453
A partly underground working producing mainly slab. Dated from 1847.
Poor rock and bad communications seem to have scarcely justified the
somewhat elaborate buildings erected in the 1890s. 34 men employed
early 1900s. Operated up to WW2, latterly employing about 5 men,
producing well under 100 tons pa. 2 saws and 2 planers.
Remains The quarrying area is much decayed and the incline formation is
scarcely visible. There are several substantial mill and other buildings of
nice architecture, but the layout is not easy to follow. Notable are the
marine tanks that were presumably used for engine fuel. (36)

SARPHLE SJ141327
Very small working.
Remains Quarry face rubbish runs, possible building remains. (29)

SPRING HILL See note re Llechwedd Gwyn.

TAN Y BWLCH = Craig Wynnstay.

TYN Y RHOS SJ074464
A tiny pit.
Remains Virtually none. (18)

TYDRAW SJ206377
Early pit working.
Remains Excavation traces. (45)

WEST LLANGYNOG SJ049259
Underground quarry with a series of adits from road level upwards.
Operated on a small scale from mid to end of 19th C. Revived by the
opening of the railway in 1904. Material from the upper adits brought
down by incline but latterly only an adit at road level was used, reduction
being done at a mill to the south of the public road. In later years a
'home-made' (diesel?) loco used. Producer gas engine running off
anthracite, powered a generator. Abandoned 1937 when pillar robbing to
meet an urgent order caused a collapse.
Remains Little in the quarry area apart from confused heaping of rubbish,
but the incline is traceable. A building is in use, possibly quarry
connected, but on the tip area to the south of the road only bases of
buildings remain. The adit at road level is collapsed, as are some others.
One adit higher up open, access may be possible. (12)

WERNDDU SJ065481
Stone quarries, possibly early use for slate.

Remains Nothing related to slate. (15)
This name also applied to Mynydd Bychan.

WESTMINSTER = Graig y Glem.

WYNNE SJ199379
Originally a hillside working dating from around 1770, developed in 1870s, underground from around 1890. Original mill buildings in a compact area with incline down to Glyn Valley Tramroad. Later an adit and mill, were built at a lower level. Peak output around 2000 tons pa with 70 men employed. Closed 1920. Used later for military storage and in 1970s opened as public display.
Remains Site and some chambers open to public. Other chambers can be visited by special arrangement. On the upper site buildings, including a fine drumhouse, are in good condition, several in reuse. An interesting collection of quarrying relics are on view, but the rake of wagons shown are coal drams.
Lower site cleared and used as car park. Adit blocked. (43)

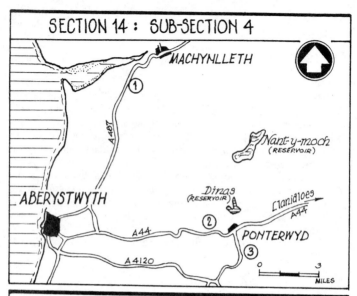

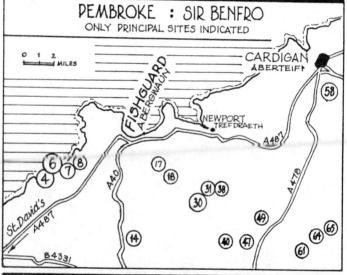

SECTION 14: SOUTH WALES/DE CYMRU

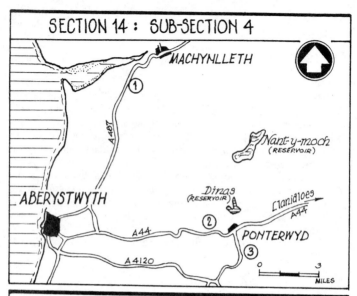

SECTION 14 : SUB-SECTION 4

MACHYNLLETH
① A487
Nant-y-moch (RESERVOIR)
ABERYSTWYTH
Dinas (RESERVOIR)
② Llanidloes A44
PONTERWYD ③
A44
A4120
0 — 3 MILES

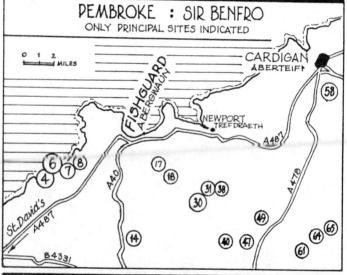

PEMBROKE : SIR BENFRO
ONLY PRINCIPAL SITES INDICATED

0 1 2 MILES
FISHGUARD ABERGWAUN
CARDIGAN ABERTEIFI
58
NEWPORT TREFDRAETH
A487
⑥ ⑦ ⑧
④
17
18
31 38
30
A40
49
A478
St. David's A487
14
40 41
64 65
61
B4331

SECTION 14: SOUTH WALES/DE CYMRU

South Wales/De Cymru Section 14

General

Almost all these quarries, the vast majority being in the north of the old county of Pembrokeshire, were very small indeed. They catered, in the main, for very local requirements, either having a very brief existence or operating only occasionally on an "as required" basis, using hand tools to produce a trifling output. There were a few which were of some significance, mechanised and with an established pattern of trade and employment. Some of these have remains that are of note.

In Pembrokeshire, the largest sites were Bellstone/Rosebush and Fforest. The most interesting, Porthgain/Abereiddy (linked by a railway). Some small, but significant, remains are at Summerton, Trwynllwyd and Llandeilo. A feature of the area is the number of cliff face sites, working between tides in isolated coves. There are, by their very nature, scant vestiges on such sites.

In the Carmarthen area, there is a (rebuilt) mill at Llwynpiod, the nearest approach to a north Wales style integrated mill, in the area.

In the Llandovery area, Chwarel Ystrad Ffin, is notable for its long and elaborate access road.

In the Builth area, Penceulan has as well as some surface remains, the only genuine underground chambering work to be seen in south Wales.

In Rheidol, in spite of its small size, Pentalwr has an incline formation.

Transport

The majority of quarries were far too small and their markets, generally too local, to have caused the development of significant transport routes. Also in contrast with Gwynedd, they were in areas already having relatively good road communications. Nevertheless some transport arrangements are of interest.

There was some, limited, use of shipping from Porthgain and several other points. There was some use made of rivers such as the Teifi to reach the sea. Many of the cliff-face quarries of north Pembroke used boat transport, but most carted using existing roads. The only tramways were the 2 mile, 3'g Porthgain-Abereiddi, horse-drawn line of circa 1860, and the much shorter Penlan and Pencelli links. All are traceable.

However, it is remarkable that two standard gauge railways were built, at least partly, to serve slate quarry needs.

The North Pembrokeshire Railway was laid down in 1876, and though later extended, was originally built almost solely to serve the Rosebush and Bellstone quarries, closed 1949, much of it is traceable.

SECTION 14: SOUTH WALES/DE CYMRU

SUB~SECTION 2

A483

⑥

⑤
③ ④

A40

A4069

LLANDOVERY
LLANYMDDYFRI

A40

① ②

0 1 2 3 4 MILES

Garreg
Ddu

Llyn
Claerwen

Caban
Coch

⑨

④ ⑥ ⑦

③

A479

A483

② ⑧

⑤

SUB~SECTION 3

A483

A481

①

BUILTH
WELLS

⑩

②

A484

A485

SUB~SECTION 1

③

④

A40

⑤

①

A40

CARMARTHEN
CAERFYRDDIN

A48

The Whitland and Cardigan Railway of 1873 was built partly to serve the Glogue, Penlan and Pencelli quarries. Closed in 1963, most of the line is traceable including the exchange siding of Pencelli and the railway yard area of Glogue.

Outside of Pembrokeshire, the one notable transport link is the magnificent cart road of Chwarel Ystrad Ffin.

Pembroke/Sir Benfro

1.	SM776304	Castellcoch
2.	798260	Trelodan
3.	798303	Cae Rhys
4.	798314	Abereiddi
5.	804328	Penclegyr
6.	813325	Porthgain
7.	817328	Henllys
8.	832329	Trwynllwyd
9.	840331	Pwll Llong
10.	864327 etc.	Trefelyn
11.	893384	Pwll Deri
12.	948336	Pantyphilip
13.	948374	Windy Hall
14.	960275	Sealyham
15.	967341	Pant y Wrach
16.	971346	Esgryn
17.	985353	Cronllwyn
18.	992302	Summerton
19.	997389	Hescwm
20.	SN010344	Cwmgwaun
21.	019399	Chwarel Pwdr
22.	020397	Chwarel Gerry
23.	026394	Fforest Farm
24.	034396	Parrog
25.	063278	Blacknuck
26.	063282	Dyffryn
27.	073231	Trebenig
28.	073282	Gotty Isaf
29.	076286	Glaslyn
30.	079300	Rosebush
31.	079302	Bellstone
32.	080313	Pantmaenog
33.	081400	Ietgoch
34.	084404	Trefach
35.	086410	Upper Mill
36.	094387	Coedcadw

37.	096284	Hafod ddu
38.	097312	Graig y Cwm
39.	098272	Temple Druid
40.	104272	Llandeilo
41.	112272	Llyn
42.	115265	Llangolman Farm
43.	119264	Pencraig
44.	124260	Clyngwyn
45.	126267 etc.	Dandderwen
46.	129263	Cwerglas
47.	130271	Llangolman
48.	131269	Gilfach Ddofn
49.	145294	Twrch
50.	147301	Castell-blaidd
51.	158297	Foel Drych
52.	158419	Llantood
53.	163442	Pant y Grundy
54.	163454	Cwmdegwell
55.	167300	Klondyke
56.	178446	Dolau
57.	180452	Ridgeway
58.	190450	Fforest
59.	192448	Rosehill
60.	198429	Dolbadau
61.	199276	Pencelli
62.	202333	Pencwarre
63.	206429	Cilgerran
64.	207284	Penlan
65.	220327	Glogue
66.	223327	Cwmgigfran
67.	226326	Cwmllwyd
68.	230324	Spite
69.	296419	Pont Ceri

Owing to there being so many tiny, ephemeral sites with a dearth of
remains, only those with worthwhile relics are mapped.

Carmarthen/Caerfyrddin
Subsection 1

1.	SN266227	Corngafr
2.	433299	Llwynpiod
3.	465224	Pantyglien
4.	535238	Eistedda Egwad
5.	603233	Dineswr

Llandovery/Llanymddyfri
Subsection 2

1.	SN713256	Coed Shon
2.	727247	Pontallechau
3.	735417	Cwm Merchon
4.	736421 etc.	Cwm Gwenlais
5.	752428	Craig Rhosan
6.	787461	Chwarel Ystradffin

Builth/Llanfair-ym-Muallt
Subsection 3

1.	SN851500	Cwm Irfon
2.	876565	Chwarel ddu
3.	892608	Esgair Ceiliog
4.	901614	Llannerch
5.	905536	Penceulan
6.	902616	Craig y Mynach
7.	912617	Moelfryn
8.	925567	Alltyddinas
9.	958637	Graig Ddu
10.	SO067479	Henallt

Rheidol
Subsection 4

1.	SN691946 etc.	Tyn y Garth
2.	741808	Pentalwr
3.	757799	Tyn y Ffordd

Llanidloes
(Not mapped)

SN844932	Dyfyngwyn

Pembroke/Sir Benfro

ABEREIDDY SM798314
A cliffside quarry with land access. Worked in 4 galleries. Originally

product was shipped straight out. After the early 1860s a 3'g horseworked tramway took material to Porthgain. Deepened into a pit, material was raised by a horse worked incline. By 1880 this was replaced by an 18hp steam engine working a lift, also powering a small mill. Closed c 1914. *Remains* The quarry pit is now open to the sea as a passage was blasted in an attempt to make a small harbour. This severed the line of the tramway and now isolates the enginehouse, mill, some dressing sheds and the stonework of the lift. Separately isolated are some of the dressing sheds remaining of the continuous line that bordered the tramway. Alongside the line are various buildings including an office or dwelling, a powder house and a forge, below rail level is Abereiddi Row (workers cottages). The rail formation round to Porthgain is readily traceable but much overgrown. (4)

BACH Part of Fforest.

BELLSTONE SN079302
Hillside quarry, virtually contiguous with Rosebush, but under separate ownership. Operated intermittently from 1825 to late 1880s. Never successful.
Remains Excavations and spoil heaps only. (31)

BLACKNUCK SN063278
Pit working, extremely small.
Remains Possible digging. (25)

CAERNAVON Part of Fforest.

CAE RHYS SM798303
Pit working, very small.
Remains Possible ground disturbance. (3)

CASTLE Part of the Cilgerran quarries.

CASTELLBLAIDD SN147301
Small pit working?
Remains None identified. (50)

CASTELLCOCH SM776304
Two tiny cliff workings.
Remains Some scarring of cliff. (1)

CAERNASH Part of Fforest.

CEFN = Cilgerran.

CILGERRAN SN206429 etc.
A series of hillside quarries on the south side of the Teifi gorge. Probably worked throughout the 19th C., possibly earlier, and up to around 1920. Latterly, at one point, material was uphauled by steam crane to a working area and machine house. A variety of ornamental, including turned, products was produced. Possibly had a short tramway. In 1850 complaints made about rubbish tipping in river.
Remains Disturbed by bulk working, little identifiable. (63)

CLYNGWYN SN124260
Hillside workings operating up to 1930s.
Remains Overgrown pit. (44)

CHWAREL GERRY SN020397
Remains Tiny overgrown pit. (22)

CHWAREL PWDR SN019399
Tiny cliffside workings, reached only by boat.
Remains Possible cliffside scarring — inaccessible. (21)

CNWC Y DERIN Part of Llangolman.

COEDCADW SN094387
Pit working?
Remains None identified. (36)

CRONLLWYN SM985353
A series of hillside workings, possibly closed by mid 19th C. rather more substantial than most in the area, but its irony product of poor cleavage was uncompetitive.
Remains No buildings on site, the tunnel which passed under the farm road from the largest of the workings has long since collapsed.
In Llanychoer there is a public house with a smithy alongside, the latter providing a tool sharpening facility for the quarrymen. It is said that a curse was put on the pub by dis-satisfied quarrymen. (17)

CWERGLAS SN129263
Tiny pit working.
Remains Ground disturbance in trees. (46)

CWMDEGWELL SN163454
Putative site.
Remains Not identified. (54)

CWMGIGFRAN SN223327
Small hillside working but believed to have (powered?) saws.
Remains Excavations and tips. (66)

CWMGWAUN SN010344
Pit working.
Remains Much overgrown, tunnel which drained the pit collapsed but traceable. (20)

CWMLLWYD SN226326
Small pit working.
Remains Ground disturbance. (67)

DANDDERWEN SN126267 & 127265
Two small hillside quarries, operated up to about 1914. One described as 'slate' the other as 'slab'.
Remains Excavations and rubbish runs. (45)

DOLBADAU SN198429
Worked the cliffs of the Teifi gorge, possibly loading directly into boats on the river. Steam crane may have been used, no explosives all material being barred out.
Remains Excavation and some spoil. (60)

DOLAU SN178446
Small hillside quarry.
Remains Slight traces of excavation. (56)

DYFFRYN SN063282
Putative site.
Remains Possible excavation. (63)

ELWYN VALLEY = Penlan.

ESGRYN SM975374 & 971346
Possibly a trial only.
Remains Not identified. (16)

FFOREST SN190450 etc.
A series of hillside workings on the south side of the Teifi Gorge, forming one of the larger, yet lesser-known, undertakings in this area.
Originally independent workings, dating from 1830s using the river for transport.
Around 1860 they were developed as a unified working connected by a riverside tramway to a mill, this tramway continuing on to carry rubbish to a tipping area on marshy ground to the west. Steam crane used. A

proper wharf was built and housing provided on site. Good rock was worked yielding a merchantable product of blue/grey colour, with, of course easy transport, but the competition of North Wales slate brought in by rail, forced closure in 1885.

The community living in the houses around the mill area survived up to the late 1920s.

The name Caernarvonshire is associated with this site, or more correctly one of the workings. This is variously stated to be because of workers coming from North Wales, or less kindly, to an attempt to pass off the product as coming from that area.

Remains The site in recent use as a wildlife park, the way in being via the trackbed of the old railway, which although it passed alongside the site, was never used by the quarry. The original access track was past Fforest house, the manager's residence.

Several buildings in the mill area have been reused but the mill itself has gone. Most of the workings are overgrown but one has a tramway/drainage tunnel some 40m long. The tramway route along the river bank is clear and there is possibly a concurrent leat. The shale built wharf is a nice feature. A limekiln, clearly much antedating the quarry is near the mill area. (58)

FFOREST FARM SN026394
Small pit working.
Remains Overgrown in woods. (23)

FFYNNON Part of Fforest.

FOELDRYCH SN158297
Hillside quarry operating in the latter part of the 19th C. Almost certainly exclusively handworked. Material carted away via Carn Wen.
Remains Excavation and one ruined building. (51)

FOREVER Part of Fforest.

GIGFRAN Part of Fforest, said to be the last to work.

GILFACH = Llangolman.

GILFACH DDOFN SN131269
Putative site.
Remains Not identified. (48)

GLASLYN SN076286
Putative site.
Remains Possible excavation. (29)

GLOGUE SN220327

A substantial hillside quarry formed by the merging of two early (17th C?) workings. Material was lowered by two inclines, the upper one being abandoned when work deepened and material was brought out to the head of the lower incline by a tunnel.

Handicapped by lack of transport, slate originally having to be carted to Blackpool on the Eastern Cleddau, and after 1853 to Narberth Road on the South Wales Railway. Expansion was only possible when in 1873 a siding on the Whitland & Cardigan Railway was laid. The owner James Owen, being one of the sponsors of that railway.

Steam and afterwards electricity was used to power the mill. Up to 84 men were employed, mainly producing slab as the roofing slates tended to be heavy, although of a good colour. During the 1920s attempts were made to produce bricks from slate dust, but they became uncompetitive when, in 1927, the G.W.R. demanded a premium due to their weight; forcing closure.

Remains Due to extensive bulk working little is to be seen, vestiges of buildings in the mill area. Virtually the only artifact is the stone built lower incline. Several dwellings, still in occupation were undoubtedly quarry houses. (65)

GOTTY ISAF SN073282

Tiny hillside quarry possibly not slate.
Remains Excavation only. (28)

GRAIG Y CWM SN097312

A series of very small hillside excavations almost 1500′ asl. It quite clearly never justified the expense of the 3 miles access road from Rosebush.
Remains Excavations and access track only. (38)

HAFOD DDU SN096284

A small pit working, water available on site but almost certainly never used. Possibility of carting material to Maenclochog station.
Remains Pit used as rubbish dump. (37)

HENLLYS SM817328

Cliffside working, no landward access, 1870s-1880s?
Remains Traces of a wall (building?) high up on cliff. (7)

HESCWM SM997389

Tiny cliffside working, material from this and other workings on the west side of the Dinas peninsular were boated, possibly to Newport.
Remains Vestiges only. (19)

IETGOCH SN081400 & 081404 (?)
Tiny pits.
Remains Possible traces of one pit. (33)

KLONDYKE SN167300
Putative site.
Remains Not identified. (55)

LILLY Most southerly of the Llandeilo quarries.

LLANDEILO SN104272 (etc.)
A series of 4 quarries, 3 to the south of, and one, the largest, to the north of the road.
The northerly one extracted poor shale like slate which was lowered by incline to a water powered mill. As the working deepened this incline route was replaced by a tunnel. The 3 southerly workings were smaller.
Remains On the main site there are vestiges of the incline formations. The 60m long tunnel is open. The mill area has been much altered but several buildings are in reuse. South of the road there is little to be seen, apart from some buildings in reuse and a nice shale built loading platform. There is an incomplete Greaves type trimmer made by Turner & Co. (40)

LLANGOLMAN SN130271 (etc.)
A series of shallow workings on either side of the river. The make was of variable quality but valued for its green colour. Still operating on a small scale in late 1980s.
Remains A few buildings, some in reuse, some tramway formation, but site is much disturbed by recent re-working. (47)

LLANGOLMAN FARM SN115265
Tiny pit.
Remains Excavation. (42)

LLANTOOD SN158419 & 157418
Very small pits.
Remains Possible excavation. (52)

LLWYN YR EBOL Most southerly of the Llangolman pits. Working 1870.

LLYN SN112272
Tiny hillside quarry, one of a number of such workings along this valley.
Remains Roadside scratching. (41)

LONG HOUSE This may be Pwll Llong or some other cliffside working.

LOWER MILL = Trefach.

PANTMAENOG SN080313
Small hillside quarry.
Remains Excavation only. (32)

PANT Y GRUNDY SN163442
Remains Possible rock-face working. (53)

PANTYPHILIP SM948336
A modest operation mainly slab and block, it has in late years been used
for bulk stone and perhaps some slab.
Remains Quarried area only. (12)

PANT Y WRACH SM967341
Possible site.
Remains Slight dip in ground. (15)

PARROG SN034396
Cliffside quarry. Material was dropped down to the beach at
Traethbroden, which was only accessible by boat. There were some
related workings at Traethsamuel, to the east of Cat Rock that were
accessible by cart at low tide. These workings were mainly producing slate
for vernacular use, and indeed there is a history in the district of roof
problems due to perishing slate. Some Parrog slate said to have been
exported from Newport in mid 18th C.
Remains Scarring of cliff face. (24)

PENCELLI SN199276
A bold late 1870s development to take advantage of the Whitland &
Cardigan Railway, material being brought down by an incline to sidings.
Lasted little more than months.
Remains Quarry area, incline, bridge under railway and sidings area. (61)

PENCLEGYR SH804328
Granite quarries using Porthgain, no slate connection. (5)

PENCWARRE SN202333
May have been tiny slate digging.
Remains Possible pit. (62)

PENLAN SN207284
A hillside working opened at the same time as Pencelli, equally
unsuccessful but did probably last into the early 1880s. Both were owned
by a Mr Bishop who had quarrying interests at Llandeilo and who was
clearly seeking to establish quarries with better transport facilities.

Finished product was taken by tramway to a siding just north of Rhydowen station.
Remains Much overgrown, vestige of a small building, tramway traceable. (64)

PENCRAIG SN119264
Putative site.
Remains Possible digging. (43)

PLAIN One of the Cilgerran workings.

PONT CERI SN296419
Small hillside working, early 20th C. A poor, shale-like product.
Remains Quarry area only. (69)

PORTHGAIN SM813325
A pit working, opened in the 1830s and developed into a self-contained community largely dependant on sea communications. Material taken down by incline to a water powered mill near the harbour. As the pit deepened, steam was used to power an uphaulage incline. This incline was later replaced by a ropeway. 16hp and 20hp engines, recorded as being in use on site, purpose of second engine unknown, but possibly it replaced the 24' mill wheel. Wind power is said to have been tried on this site.
When, at the turn of the century, the slate deteriorated into shales, these were used for brick making, uphaulage out of the pit being avoided by a tunnel, which by running below-pit bottom level enabled drams to be loaded by chutes. Another diversification was the construction of brick hoppers to load granite brought from a quarry on the nearby headland by a locomotive powered railway. The entire enterprise closed in the early 1930s.
Remains The large pit itself and the incline down to the mill. The railway formation round to Abereddi and the mill with wheelpit (and an interesting lavatory above the tailrace), a particularly fine slate leat and several other buildings which are in reuse. Most of the dwellings are still occupied and the little harbour office is a pleasing structure. To the east of the village are the remains of the brick kilns. The tunnel from the harbour to under the pit is still open.
The brick built hoppers are a most prominent feature, behind them are numerous remains from the granite operation, including a loco shed. (6)

PORTH Y MEIBION = Cae Rhys.

PRECELLY = Bellstone.

PWDR Part of Cilgerran.

PWLL DERI SM893384
Two tiny cliffside workings.
Remains Scarring of cliffs. (11)

PWLL LLONG SM840331
Tiny cliffside workings.
Remains Scarring of cliff face. (9)

RIDGEWAY SN180452
Putative working.
Remains Not identified. (57)

ROSEBUSH SN079300
The only undertaking in the region to operate on anything like a scale and certainly the only one to have its own railway. A series of ancient hillside workings, developed on 4 levels by Edward Cropper in the mid 1870s who built the Narberth Road to Maenclochog Railway mainly to serve this quarry.
A mill near the railhead was water turbine powered. Wind power is said to have been tried at one time, (for pumping?). Production declined in the 1880s and final closure came in 1914.
Remains There is surprising little to be seen on this fairly extensive site. The workings are much degraded and there is no sign of the incline or of the, at least one, access tunnel. Near the railway terminus, which became a branch after the extension to Letterston, the loco shed still stands, there are a few other buildings, including, possibly the mill with pipework for the turbine supply.
Many of the houses in the village were quarry houses and are mostly still in occupation. The Precelli Hotel is still in its temporary galvanised sheet form. The ornamental gardens and pond laid out to attract visitors after the fortunes of the quarry declined are overgrown but still visible. (30)

ROSEHILL SN192448
A hillside working on opposite side of river from Fforest, may have been worked in conjunction.
Remains Spoil only. (59)

ST BRIDE'S This name used for both Abereiddi and Porthgain S Qs.

SEALYHAM SM960275
A pit working operating from 1825 to 1885 which can scarcely have provided a return on the substantial investment made.
Material was hauled out of the pit originally possibly by water power which was used to power the mill and the pump. There being a substantial diversion of the river to provide supply.
Steam was introduced in the early 1870s together with other ambitious

developments. Finished slate was carted to Haverfordwest for shipment.
Remains The pit is flooded and the site is heavily overgrown. There are numerous traces of buildings and other structures but it is difficult to make any positive identification or trace working methods. (14)

SUMMERTON SM992302

A substantial hillside working from about 1830, deepened into a pit with a cutting access, which also drained. Then, as the workings became deeper still, some kind of ropeway was used to haul out. It seems to have possibly had a tramway leading to a water powered mill. The underground workings are believed to be subsequent trials for metal. Closed 1880s.
Remains A somewhat enigmatic site. In the face of the pit are two adits, neither of which penetrated far. Immediately to the west is a structure that could have been a winding house for a slant, and some 300m north is a filled in square shaft. There is no evidence that this underground work was seeking slate.

On either side of the pit are pillars perhaps for an aerial ropeway. In front of the pit there was at one time a quantity of trimming waste, suggesting that reduction was done there.

A causeway 250m long runs to the west, described as a dam it appears to be a tramway leading to ruined buildings, although at the quarry end the levels are wrong.

These ruined buildings, much overgrown, include a curious structure resembling a two arched bridge, its purpose is not clear but could be the mounting of a water powered sandsaw. Downhill are further building traces and a possible wheelpit.

The leat system, immediately uphill from this presumed works area has been ploughed up. (18)

SPITE SN230324
Small pit.
Remains Pit much overgrown. (68)

TEILO VALE Part of the Llandeilo workings.

TEMPLE DRUID SN098272
Small hillside quarry, operated into 20th C. Water power may have been used for sawing using ancient fish ponds as supply.
Remains Excavation, possible building foundations. (39)

TOMMY Part of Fforest.

TONGE Part of Fforest.

TREBENIG SN073231
Tiny pit.
Remains Lost in forestry. (27)

TREFACH SN084404
Tiny, possibly very early.
Remains Traces of digging. (34)

TREFELYN SM864327 & 868326
Putative sites.
Remains Possible tiny diggings. (10)

TRELODAN SM798260
Suggestions that there was some slate extraction here circa 1860.
Remains Lost by airfield construction. (2)

TRWYNLLWYD SM832329
Cliffside terraced quarry operated in conjunction with Porthgain in the
latter part of 19th C. Steam power (10hp) used for both mill and winding.
Remains Quarry area virtually inaccessible. At clifftop is a nice little mill
building with engine or boiler house alongside. The incline is visible but
degraded, the rock being cut out to give a straight haul. At its head is the
base for a haulage sheave. The waste runs contain circular sawn ends. (8)

TWRCH SN145294
A substantial undertaking with a pit to the east of the road connected by a
tunnel to a mills area to the west of the road.
Originally water powered, latterly IC engine used.
Produced a unique grainy grey slate. Closed in 1930s with failure of the
Campbell company.
Remains The tunnel has been replaced by a pipe. Traces of some early
buildings also some later buildings, partly brick built, in reuse. (49)

UPPER MILL SN086410
Small pit working.
Remains Possible ground disturbance. (35)

VAGUR = Hafod Ddu.

WINDY HALL SM948374
Possible slate site.
Remains Not identified. (13)

CORNGAFR SN266227
Tiny quarry of convenience.
Remains Excavation, nearby farm buildings are of great interest. (1)

EISTEDDA EGWAD SH535238
Hillside quarry, very small, marginal material.
Remains Possible building. (4)

DINESWR SN603233
Mention of slate quarrying here 1767.
Remains Possible traces at this location. (5)

LLWYNPIOD SN433299
Pit working. Mention in 1833 of two quarries in Abergwili area employing 50 men making roofing slates (Lewis), 1841, this quarry mentioned by name. The steam powered mill, containing 3 machines, possibly 2 saws and a planer, powered by a horizontal steam engine, undoubtedly dates from 1864 when the Pant y Glien Slate & Slab Co. made a big investment. Material originally trammed in direct from the quarry, later, as the pit deepened, by a haulage. Oddly, only one door of the mill seems to have been used for all traffic.
When the rubbish area to the south of the mill became full, a bridge was built to permit tipping to the east of the road.
The pit was drained to the stream by a tunnel about 120m long.
A coarse and heavy roofing slate, was produced, and latterly slabs, lintels etc., much in evidence in the locality. Building blocks were also produced. Fines were used for brick making at Carmarthen. Closed 1920s.
Remains The fine mill building has been rebuilt for reuse. The mountings for the gantry over the 3 machine positions can be seen. There is space for trimmers but it is doubtful if these were installed. There is a platform, for the engine in one corner and behind the building a boiler house with base of demolished stack. There is an underfloor cistern, and some drains, which also seem to have served an adjacent building. The pit having been filled there is no trace of the incline but there is some evidence of a rope connection to the mill engine to power it.
There is possible trace of the outlet end of the tunnel. The tip on the far side of the road was largely removed to provide hardcore when Penysarn estate was built. (2)

PANTYGLIEN SN465224
Small hillside working, possibly 18th C. In latter 19th C., in common

ownership with Llwynpiod. Probably entirely unmechanised.
Remains Quarry face only. (3)

Llandovery/Llanymddyfri
Subsection 2

COED SHON SN713256
Small pit working, shales?
Remains Possible digging. (1)

CHWAREL YSTRAD FFIN SN787461
A 'Classic' hillside quarry, deepened into a pit which was accessed by a tunnel, mostly shale but some material of a good colour and split.
Remains Extensive rubbish runs, vestiges of several dressing sheds, but the tunnel has vanished under a massive slide. The access track 2km long, well engineered with nice retaining walling, is most spectacular. (6)

CRAIG RHOSAN SN752428
A small working of shales bearing some cleavage material. In grounds of Neuadd Fawr. (1784)
Remains Excavation, waste, working platform and access track. (5)

CWM GWENLAIS (1) SN737422, 736421 & 742423
The first two are tiny underground workings, the more easterly may have produced saleable product. The third is a slot working a band of shale-like rock about 1 metre wide, very much like a metal mine.
Remains The westerly adit is collapsed, the easterly is a cave like working with some possible trimming waste on the rubbish run. The slot working seems to be deep as there is a considerable volume of waste. There are the abutments of an access track bridge. (4)

CWM MERCHON SN735417
Small hillside working.
Remains Dressing shed. (3)

PONTALLECHAU SN727247
Hillside quarry of complex geology, possibly some slate.
Remains Interesting quarry face, bases of stone crushers. (2)

Builth/Llanfair-ym-Muallt
Subsection 3

ALLTYDDINAS SN925567
Small surface workings, some underground?
A number of very shallow workings exploiting outcrops of shales. The reduction process seems to have been mainly by selection and trimming with little or no splitting. Probably a quarry of convenience operating over many years. Work possibly ceased around 1860.
Material carted via Cwmdulais Farm.
Remains At least 6 extraction points with associated dressing areas. Tips but no buildings. Lowest working has an adit (open) which seems to have been a trial.
One of the upper dressing floors has a large stock of, much decayed, product, mainly taper top moss-slates.
Original cart track traceable. (8)

CHWAREL DDU SN876565
Primitive operation of a scarp exposure.
Remains Virtually none apart from zig-zag access path.
Early slates in Elan Valley identified with this source. (2)

CRAIG Y MYNACH SN902616
Tiny working by roadside.
Remains Traces of excavation. (6)

CWM IRFON SN851500
Small pit working possibly as late as 1890s.
Remains In forestry but tips and some vestige of access road. (1)

ESGAIR CEILIOG SN892608
Several workings in a tiny rift valley, possible some underground.
Remains Dressing sheds, some rail on ground, large quantity of waste.
Unidentified building at valley mouth. (3)

GRAIG DDU SN958637
Possibly very small scale extraction.
Remains Interesting anticline dynamic metamorphosis formation. (9)

HENALLT SO067479
Open quarry, latterly (early 20th C.) producing shale building block identified in nearby housing. May have yielded roofing material.
Remains Excavation only. (10)

LLANNERCH SN901614
Very small working, possibly some underground.
Remains Dressing sheds on 2 levels. (4)

MOELFRYN SN912617
Small hillside working.
Remains Much degraded quarry face. Working area has been cleared.
Access track. (7)

PENCEULAN SN905536
Open quarry/underground. An old quarry of convenience with a notable
attempt, in 1880s, to chamber work in Meirionnydd manner, material
carted down valley.
Remains A series of working faces seemingly haphazardly developed in
confused rock conditions, with dressing sheds, two sets being in rakes of
three.
Adjacent to the upper adit are some buildings including a weighbridge
and what may have been a small mill. Possible unfinished incline. This
adit penetrates about 50 metres. Part way along a start was made on a cross
heading along the strike, opposite this is a strike tunnel from which there
are two roofing shafts cut up the dip, one sound, the other collapsed. No
extraction appears to have been made.
Lower down site there were possibly two other levels with adits
collapsed/tipped over.
At lowest level there is a further adit leading to 2 small chambers one of
which opens up to level above, which has been worked out to bank. (5)

Rheidol
Subsection 4

CADLO = Pentalwr.

PENTALWR SN741808
Hillside quarry, very shaley product.
Remains Intense folding on working face exposure. Drumhouse,
masonry. Incline formation which cut through disused Llanwernog lead
mine leats. (2)

TYN Y FFORDD SN757799
Hillside quarry.
Remains Excavation only, intense local folding with some cleavable
material. (3)

TYN Y GARTH SN691946 & 692947
Putative sites.
Remains Some excavation but unlikely to have been slate. (1)

Llanidloes

DYFYNGWYN SN844932
Old hillside quarry, possibly slate.
Remains Excavation only.

Also putative sites 951855, 929868 90x90x 89x00x 847931.

Glossary

Welsh terms are included where they are commonly used and where the English equivalent is not obvious. Many are unique to the industry.

adit	The entrance to a tunnel.
Anderson	A type of saw.
back-filling	Underground technique of packing waste into disused chambers, rather than taking it to surface.
bad rock	Any non-slate rock encountered during quarrying.
balanced incline	An incline with two tracks, where the weight of a downgoing load raised upgoing empties. Obviously only of use for downgoing loads.
barrack	Building where men lodged, usually on a Monday to Saturday basis, but occasionally unmarried men lived permanently.
bar rail	Rail track consisting of plain rectangular iron bar.
bedding plane	The original sedimentary plane of the rock.
black powder	Gun powder, used for extracting rock.
block	Slate rock, possibly roughly trimmed, as sent from the quarrying face, prior to reduction.
blondin	A wire rope spanning a pit working. Hoisting gear mounted on a carriage on that rope, enabled loads to be raised and travelled. A sophistication of the chain incline.
brake	Device for controlling movement on an incline. Usually in the case of a drum, a simple strap, occasionally, contracting shoes. With a sheave, generally a shoe forced into the rope-groove.
ceir gwyllt	Device enabling a person to ride (rapidly!) down an incline.
celfi naddu	The fixed iron blade, used in conjunction with the cyllell for hand-trimming roofing slate.
chain incline	An incline running on chain or wire-rope instead of rails, used for pit workings as it could readily be resited.
chamber	An underground working typically 70′ wide.
chwarel	General name for any quarry.
cleavage	The plane in which the slate splits, desirably at as large an angle as possible to the bedding plane.
cloddfa	Quarry, usually underground.
Cooke	Patentee of tunnelling and other machinery.
cowjian	Plug chisel used for splitting blocks.
crane	Commonly, a sheer-legs structure for handling blocks near the quarrying face. Rarer, a derrick for raising loads from a pit working. Also the overhead cranes for handling slate within a mill. Rarely were any powered.
crimp	The extreme edge of the top of an incline.
crimp sprag	Device to prevent trucks running away down an incline.
cupboarding	Cutting into pillars to cheaply obtain slate.
cyllell naddu	The knife-like tool for the hand-trimming of roofing slate.
cŷn brashollt	Wide chisel for splitting blocks.
cŷn manhollt	Wide and slim chisel used for splitting roofing slates.

De Winton	A Caernarfon firm noted for vertical boilered locomotives, non-rotative trimmers, saws and other machinery.
dip	The direction in which a vein inclines downwards.
Dixon, E.J.J.	Patentee of an experimental tunnelling machine, also an early man-powered rock drill and several types of saw.
double-flanged wheel	A wheel, loose on an axle intended either to conform to variations in gauge of temporary track, or to adapt to differing gauges.
dressing shed	An open-fronted structure, where roofing slates were split and trimmed. Occasionally for trimming blocks. If the latter, then usually was a larger structure.
drum	The horizontal drum, 5-8′ long x 2-3′ dia, usually of cast-iron with staves; around which the rope of a balanced incline was wound.
drumhouse	The structure supporting the drum or sheaves of a balanced incline. Usually it spanned the tracks (through drumhouse). Some did not span tracks (remote drumhouse).
firesetting	Primitive method of breaking rock for tunnelling, by heating and then quenching.
flat rods	Horizontal rods, usually with intermediate supports, used to operate a pump a distance from a (usually water) power source.
floor	Working level of a quarry (usually underground).
gang saw	A frame-carried array of reciprocating saw blades, to make multiple cuts in a block or slab.
gloddfa	A "digging", sometimes applied to underground quarries.
gordd y twll	Sledge-type hammer used for breaking rock.
Greaves	Besides owning Llechwedd quarry, this firm developed several machines, notably the widely used Greaves rotative trimmer, normally powered, could be treadle worked.
hollti	The splitting (of slate).
horse whim	An overhead drum on a vertical axis, powered by a horse walking in a circle around it. Used for raising loads, extremely rare in the slate industry.
Hughes	A form of round-section bar rail, secured at its end by bent-down spigots. Also name of an early trimming machine.
Hunter	A heavy circular saw, with replaceable teeth. Unusual in that the overtable saw was fixed and the table moved. Also name of a tunnel boring machine.
jwmpah	A long weighted rod (usually around 2 metres, but could be much longer). Used, by repeatedly thrusting, to bore a shot-hole.
launder	Elevated trough for carrying water.
leat	Channel in the ground for carrying water.
llechi	Literally flat stones, but used as name for both slate rock and roofing slates.
marcio	Marking, both in the sense of scratching where a slate is to be trimmed and the incising of a block to facilitate splitting.
mass balanced incline	A single acting balanced table incline where an iron weight usually running on a narrow track between the table rails, counterbalanced a downgoing load.

mwrthwl dragio	A short hammer used for driving wedges to break rock.
Matthews	A very large powered, guillotine type, trimmer.
integrated mill	A building where several operations in the reduction of slate is carried out. Usually at least sawing, splitting and trimming.
mill	Any building where the reduction of slate is carried out using machinery.
miniar	A very stubby chisel used for splitting rock.
mochyn	The iron weighted balancing trolley of a mass balanced incline.
Owen	Several entirely unconnected 'Owens' made various saws and other machinery, the best known is John Owen of Bangor.
pelton wheel	A power source whereby a jet of water propelled a rotor.
pillar	The area of slate left undisturbed between chambers of an underground working to support the ground above.
pillar robbing	The bad practice of thinning pillars underground to cheaply obtain slate.
pillaring line	Line of weakness in rock, facilitating the removal of blocks.
pillaring machine	Frame to assist the drilling of a number of closely spaced holes to create an artificial pillaring line.
pin-down pillar	The pillar, with holes used to secure a brake-lever on an (usually table-type) incline.
planer	Machine for smoothing the surface of a slab of slate.
plate rail	Angle iron rail intended for unflanged wheeled trucks, very rare in Welsh quarries.
plwg ac adain	A tool consisting of an inner tapered pin surrounded by a split shell, which when hammered into a crevice, will expand.
polisher	Machine for fine finishing slabs, modern ones have diamond impregnated blocks which are rotated, older ones used sand.
ponc	A terrace in a quarry.
powder house	Explosives store (Tŷ Pwdr).
powered incline	A single acting uphaulage incline operated by steam, electricity or rotative water power. Could have several tracks.
pric mesur	The serrated stick, with a nail at one end used for marking out a roofing slate for trimming.
pump	Almost invariably an immersed force-pump, operated by vertical rods, rarely, a rag and chain pump, with an endless chain pulling greased rags through a vertical pipe. Occasionally a bucket pump, with buckets on an endless chain.
quarry of convenience	Site in occasional use for local requirements.
reduction	The processes of converting raw blocks into saleable product.
rock cannon	A number of shallow holes in a rock, joined by grooves, when filled with black powder would produce a series of explosions. Used to mark special occasions.
roofing shaft	The first cut made in developing a chamber, made along the top of the vein, usually on the right of the intended extraction area. Normally made from a strike tunnel.
Rhys	A massive, iron bound, African oak mallet which skillfully used could break a block.

rubbish	Any non-useable rock or trimmings.
rubbish run	A tipping area. Normally railed with tipping point at the end.
rwblwr	The unskilled man or young learner who removed waste rock.
sandsaw	A toothless reciprocating saw that cut by the introduction of sand into the kerf. Might be hand held or mechanically oscillated in a frame.
saw	A machine for reducing blocks to rectangular slabs. Other than sandsaws (above), almost always a moving table with a circular iron or steel blade protruding from underneath. Very occasionally hand-cranked. If modern, then fixed table with a moving (diamond) saw above the table.
self-acting	A balanced incline.
incline sheave	A grooved pulley wheel, occasionally used instead of a drum at the head of a balanced incline. Set with on vertical axle, either in an underfloor pit, or in a "drumhouse". If underground, almost invariably with the axle horizontal. Also, used at any point where a rope was turned such as a bottom-wound haulage incline.
shot	Explosive charge.
sinc	A pit working.
single-acting incline	A powered incline, with only one track. Normally of the table type. Could be either for raising or lowering.
slab	A piece of finished or part finished, slate thicker and larger than a roofing slate.
slatau	Properly, a writing slate, but also loosely applied to any slate product.
sledge	An early device for moving finished product down a mountainside. Guided by a rider.
slideway	An un-railed incline.
splitting	The hand operation of separating a block of slate into roofing material or thin slab. Or, the reduction of a block into smaller pieces other than by sawing.
strike	A horizontal direction at righ angles to the dip.
strike tunnel	A tunnel bored, horizontally along the strike, to enable a series of underground chambers to be developed.
table incline	An incline where one or more trucks are carried on a table rather than running on the incline rails themselves.
take-note	Authority from a landowner for an individual or partnership to extract.
terrace	Elevated working level of an open-air quarry.
three-ply dam	The usual method of dam construction, two walls, with a clay filling.
Tom & Gerry Engine	A device whereby a tank of water filled to operate a pump, usually through flat rods.
trimmer	Machine for trimming slates to size, usually the powered, rotative Greaves type, less commonly the De Winton guillotine type (power or treadle operated).
trunc	The table of a table incline.
Turner & Co.	A firm in Newtown, Powis, a famous maker of slate mill machinery, their circular saws were widely used.
turntree	A windlass, either man or animal powered.

twll	A pit working.
untopping	Removing the overburn of an underground working to enable the slate pillars to be removed. Modern machinery makes this economic.
wal	A shed, usually open fronted, where slate was split and trimmed.
wallet	A cloth double sack, carried on the shoulder. Used by barracking men to carry their food supplies for the week.
waste	Any unusuable rock or trimmings.
water balance	An inclined or vertical means of raising a load, employing the weight of a downgoing tank of water, which usually, but not exclusively, travelled parallel with the load.
winch	A portable device for pulling, or in conjunction with a sheave, lifting. Usually hand, steam or air powered, common underground, rarer in surface workings.
winding house	The structure supporting or enclosing the drum or sheaves of powered incline.
weighbridge or weigh-house	Weighing machine, usually for waste, to assess rwblwr's pay.
Williams	Early type of trimming machine.

Traditional names for sizes of slate, (inches)
(Varied slightly from area to area, these are Blaenau standards)

Empresses	26 x 16
Princesses	24 x 14
Dutchesses	24 x 12
Small Dutchesses	22 x 12
Marchionesses	22 x 11
Countesses	20 x 10
Viscountesses	18 x 9
Wide Ladies	16 x 10
Broad Ladies	16 x 9
Ladies	16 x 8
Small Ladies	14 x 8
Narrow Ladies	14 x 7

Terms Singles, Doubles, Headers etc. used for smaller sizes.

Selected Bibliography

Baughan, P.E., *A Regional History of the Railways of G.B. Vols 11 & 12*, David & Charles, 1980.

Bingley, W.A., *A Journal of a Tour through North Wales etc.*, London, 1797.

Boyd, J.I.C., *Narrow Gauge Railways in Mid Wales*, Oakwood, 1970.

Boyd, J.I.C., *Narrow Gauge Railways in South Caernarfonshire*, Oakwood, 1972.

Boyd, J.I.C., *The Ffestiniog Railways Vols 1 & 2*, 1975.

Boyd, J.I.C., *Narrow Gauge Railways in North Caernarfonshire Vols 1, 2 & 3*, Oakwood, 1981/6.

Boyd, J.I.C., *Tal-y-Llyn Railway*, Wild Swan, 1988.

Christiansen, R., *The Forgotten Railways of North & Mid Wales*, David & Charles, 1976.

Davies, D.C., *Slate & Slate Quarrying*, Crosby, Lockwood, 1878.

Davies, D.L., *The Glyn Valley Tramway, Oakwood*, 1962.

Dodd, A.H., *The Industrial Revolution in North Wales*, University of Wales Press, 1971.

Holmes, A., *Slates from Abergynolwyn*, Gwynedd Archive Service, 1986.

Holmes & Thomas, *Quarry Tracks, Village Ways*, Talyllyn Railway Co., 1977.

Hughes & Hughes, *Chwarel y Penrhyn*, Chwarel y Penrhyn, 1979.

Isherwood, G., *Candles to Caplamps*, Gloddfa Ganol, 1980.

Isherwood, G., *Cwmorthin Slate Quarry*, Merioneth F.S. Press, 1982.

Isherwood, G., *Slate*, A.B. Publishing, 1988.

Jermy, R.C., *The Railways of Porthgain & Abereiddi*, Oakwood Press, 1986.

Jones, E., *Bargen Dinorwig*, Tŷ ar y Graig, 1980.

Jones, I.W., *Llechwedd Slate Caverns*, Quarry Tours, 1976.

Jones, I.W. & G. Hetherill, *Llechwedd and other Ffestiniog Railways*, Quarry Tours, 1977.

Jones, R.M., *The North Wales Quarrymen 1874-1922*, Cardiff University of Wales, 1982.

Kellow, J., *The Slate Trade of North Wales*, Mining Journal, 1868.

Lee, C., *The Welsh Highland Railway*, Welsh Highland Railway, 1970.

Lee, C., *The Penrhyn Railway*, Welsh Highland Railway, 1972.

Lewis, M.J.T., *Early Wooden Railways*, R.K.P., 1970.

Lewis, M.J.T., *Llechi, Slates*, Gwynedd Archive Service, 1976.

Lewis, M.J.T. (Ed), *The Slate Quarries of North Wales in 1873*, S.N.P.S.C., 1987.

Lewis, M.J.T., *Sails on the Dwyryd*, S.N.P.S.C., 1989.

Lewis & Denton, *Rhosydd Slate Quarry*, Cottage Press, 1974.

Lewis & Williams, *Pioneers of Welsh Slate*, S.N.P.S.C., 1987.

Lindsay, J., *The History of the North Wales Slate Industry*, David & Charles, 1974.

Lindsay, J., *The Great Strike*, David & Charles, 1987.

Lloyd, Lewis, *The Port of Caernarfon 1793-1900*, Gwasg Pantycelyn, 1989.

Morris, J.P., *The North Pembrokeshire & Fishguard Railway*, Oakwood, 1969.

North, F.J., *Slates of Wales*, National Museum of Wales, 1925.

Owen, R., *Diwydiannau Coll.*

Parry, B.R. (Ed), *Chwareli a Chwarelwyr*, Gwynedd Archive Service, 1974.

Price, M.R.C., *The Whitland and Cardigan Railway*, Oakwood, 1976.

Rees, D.M., *The Industrial Archaeology of Wales*, David & Charles, 1975.

Richards, M., *Slate Quarrying and how to Make it Profitable.*

Roberts, A., *Round and About Porthgain*, Abercastle Publishers, 1979.

Tomos, D., *Llechi Lleu*, Argraffdy Arfon, 1980.
Turner, S., *The Padarn and Penrhyn Railways*, David & Charles, 1975.
Williams, G.J., *Hanes Plwyf Ffestiniog*, Hughes & Son, 1882.
Williams & Lewis, *Gwydir Slate Quarries*, S.N.P.S.C., 1989.
Williams & Lewis, *Pioneers of Ffestiniog Slate*, S.N.P.S.C., 1987.
Williams & Lewis, *Chwarelwyr Cyntaf Ffestiniog*, S.N.P.S.C., 1987.
Wren, W.J., *The Tanat Valley*, David & Charles, 1968.

S.N.P.S.C. = Snowdonia National Park Study Centre, Plas Tan y Bwlch.

Reports

Report of the Departmental Committee upon Merionethshire Slate Mines, 1895.
Plas Tan y Bwlch Report on Chwarel Diffwys (Unpublished), 1983.
Plas Tan y Bwlch Report on Cwt y Bugail and Blaen y Cwm (Unpublished), 1985.
Plas Tan y Bwlch Report on Chwarel Foel and Chwarel Rhos (Unpublished), 1986.

Journals

The Old Slate Industry of Pembrokeshire and other parts of South Wales.
Tucker, G. & M., 'The slate industry of Pembrokeshire and its borders', *Ind. Arch. Review* 3, 1979.
Tucker, G. & M., *The National Library of Wales Journal*, XXIII No. 2, 1983.
The Gwernor Slate Quarry, Nantlle Jones, G.P., (Unpublished).
Transactions of the Caernarfonshire Historical Society, 1987.